NorthParadePublishing

4 North Parade,
Bath BA11LF. UK
Printed in China.
www.nppbooks.co.uk

Image Credits:
Shutterstock Images.
Top: t, Middle: m, Left: l, Right: r, Bottom: b
Pages: 18t, 38b, 53tr, 72-73bm, 97tl, 97tr, 104l, 105bl, 121.

Encyclopedia of Natural Disasters

A Complete Guide To Natural Disasters

CONTENTS

Fire & Flood

Nature's Fury	8
Fire	10
Forests on Fire	12
Wildfires in History	13
Battling Wildfires	14
Buildings on Fire	16
Safety Precautions	18
Dos and Don'ts	20
Call the Fire Department	22
Towns on Fire	24
Fire Timeline	26
River Floods	28
Wrath of the Sea	30
Flash Floods	32
Flood Control	34
Flood Forecast	35
To the Rescue	36
Myths and Legends	37

Hurricanes & Tornadoes

Atmosphere	38
The Weather Goes Wild	40
Watching the Wind	42
Weather at Sea	44
Here Comes the Hurricane	46
Calm Before the Storm	48
Hurricane Wary	49
Disaster Strikes	50
A Twisted Story	52
Chasing the Storm	53
Tornado Alley	54
Safety and Rescue	55
Spinning out of Control	56
Hurricanes vs Tornadoes	58
Stormy Side Effects	59
Forecasting at First	60
Forecasting and Observation	61
Super Survivors	63
In Legend and Fiction	65

Volanoes & Earthquakes

Inside the earth	67
Volcanoes	68
Volcano Classification	70
Volcanoes Under Sea	71
Rocks and Minerals	72
Geysers and Hot Springs	74
Extraterrestrial Volcanoes	76
Famous Volcanoes	77
More Famous Volcanoes	78
Volcanology	79
Volcanoes and the Weather	81
Earthquakes	82
Famous Earthquakes	83
Measuring Earthquakes	85
Features of Volcanoes and Earthquakes	86
In Preparation	88
Rescue Mission	90
Legends	92
Fascinating Facts	94

Wild & Weather

What's the Weather Like?	96
Sun and Water	98
Wind and Cloud	100
Seasons	102
Climates	103
Humid and Hot	104
Storming the Skies	106
Thunder and Lightning	108
Weather Wash	110
As Cold as Can Be	112
Snow, Hail and Ice	113
When Storms Strike	114
Drought Disasters	116
Weather Watch	117
Eye in the Sky	119
Changing Weather	120
Weather Woes	121
Weather or What!	123
Fascinating Facts	124

Nature's Fury

Earthquakes, volcanic eruptions, storms, hurricanes, blizzards, fires and floods are all examples of natural disasters. Of these, fire and flood are probably the most common disasters to have plagued the world.

When the Earth Trembles

Earthquakes are one of the main causes of fires. During an earthquake the ground trembles. A severe tremor can cause objects to be knocked down, and even lead huge buildings to crumble. In the event, a broken electric line or kitchen equipment that has been knocked over, is enough to start a fire.

▸ *Broken electrical or gas lines during an earthquake frequently cause fires.*

Fire from Beneath

Volcanoes can also cause fires. When a volcano erupts, it releases molten lava along with ash and mud. Lava is rock that has been melted due to the high temperatures inside the Earth's surface. When this liquid rock flows through towns and cities, the heat can set fire to the surrounding trees and houses.

▾ *Lava flowing out of a volcano can set fire to trees and surrounding vegetation.*

Rising Waters

Floods are usually caused by heavy rainfall, storms, or excessive melting of snow or ice. Earthquakes can also cause floods in coastal regions. Floods can be accompanied by landslides. As the water loosens mud, rocks and other materials on a slope or hill, these may start to slide down.

▼ *Heavy floods can sweep away trees, houses, vehicles and people.*

INTERESTING FACT

On December 15, 1999, Venezuela witnessed the worst natural disaster in its history. About 10,000 people reportedly died in floods that swept through the country for a week. Most of them died in landslides.

FACT FILE

THE WORST NATURAL DISASTERS EVER

- Flood: 1887; Hwang Ho River, China; over 900,000 dead
- Earthquake: 1556; Shensi Province, China; over 830,000 killed
- Hurricane: 1970; East Pakistan (Bangladesh); 500,000-1,000,000 dead
- Landslide: 1920; Kansu, China; more than 180,000 killed
- Volcano: 1815; Mt. Tambora, Indonesia; over 90,000 killed
- Forest fire: 1871; Peshtigo, Wisconsin, US; about 1,500 dead

Global Warming

Global warming is the phenomenon of an unnatural rise in the Earth's temperature. The cause is an enhanced 'greenhouse effect' – the trapping of heat in the Earth's atmosphere. It is known that the Earth radiates back part of the Sun's heat it receives. However, certain gases in the atmosphere, such as water vapour and carbon dioxide, prevent the heat from escaping into space. It is such greenhouse gases that have kept our planet warm.

▶ *Human activities like deforestation and fuel burning are increasing the amount of greenhouse gases, leading to overheating of the Earth. This can cause heat waves, melting of glaciers, and a rise in sea levels – and result in fire and flood disasters.*

Fire

Fire was one of the most important discoveries in the history of mankind. It helps us cook food and keeps us warm during the long winters. However, if not handled carefully, fire can also wreak havoc. A fire that is out of control can be as dangerous as any other natural disaster, creating mass destruction of both life and property.

Fuelling the Fire

Three elements are essential for a fire to survive – fuel, oxygen and heat. In forests, trees and other plants act as fuel. In buildings, the fuel source can be books, papers and furniture. Oxygen is essential for fire to survive. Also, the fire would die if there was no heat to sustain it. The flame emitted during a fire produces heat, which in turn heats the remaining fuel – making the fire grow.

Gases and Flames

Fire can be divided into four parts: gas, flame, heat and smoke. Certain poisonous gases like carbon monoxide are released during a fire. These are known as fire gases. Flame is the light that can be seen due to the burning of gas. Heat is the warmth that you feel while sitting next to a fire. But if you get too close, the heat can also burn you. A normal fire emits heat of about 1,100 degrees Celsius.

◀ *The fire triangle*

▲ *It is said that early man rubbed flints together to set fire to pieces of wood.*

Smoke Alarm!

Smoke is a harmful cloud of vapour mixed with powdered particles generated by a fire. More people die by inhaling smoke and poisonous gases, than from actual burns.

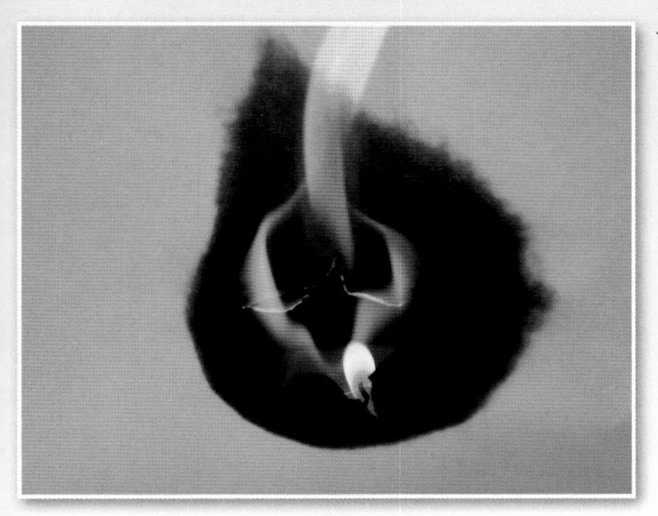

◀ *The temperature at which a material ignites is called the flashpoint. The flashpoint of paper is 233 degrees Celsius.*

Up in Flames

Fire can be caused by human negligence or by natural forces like lightning, droughts, earthquakes and volcanoes. A huge fire that burns down towns and cities is known as a conflagration. Firestorms are huge fires produced by several separate fires burning at the same time.

▼ *Uncontrolled fires can reach temperatures as high as 1,500 degrees Celsius.*

INTERESTING FACT

It is believed that man accidentally discovered fire about 1.5 million years ago. Apparently he made fire by rubbing two flints together. At first, man used fire to scare animals away. Eventually he started to use it to warm the cave and cook food.

FACT FILE

POLITICAL FIRES

- 1812: Following Napoleon's invasion, the residents of Moscow evacuate the city, deliberately setting many of the buildings on fire
- 1814: The residence of the president of the United States, today known as the White House, is burned down by the British army
- 1865: Retreating Confederate Army set fire to the city of Richmond, Virginia, during the American Civil War
- 1933: Marinus van der Lubbe, a communist, sets fire to the Reichstag, the seat of German Parliament, in Berlin
- 1991: Retreating Iraqi armed forces set fire to oil wells in Kuwait, following the Persian Gulf War

Forests on Fire

Wildfires, also known as forest fires, occur in natural settings like forests, woods and grasslands. They usually occur in places that experience long periods of hot, dry weather. These places also have a sufficiently moist climate to support the growth of trees and vegetation. Wildfires can rage through thousands of acres of land within minutes, destroying everything in their path.

Spread Like a Wildfire

The spread of wildfires depends on the type and amount of fuel in the region. Fuel could be a piece of wood, logs, or even houses. The amount of material that can catch fire in a given area is called fuel load. The larger the fuel load, the faster the fire spreads.

Unless put out properly, embers from campfires can cause a fire up to several days later.

Causes

Wildfires are sometimes caused by the heat of the sun and lightning. However, most fires are the result of human carelessness. Campfires not put out properly, and discarded cigarettes or matchsticks can result in raging wildfires.

Discarded cigarettes can unwittingly cause a forest fire.

Good and Bad Fires

Wildfires can be classified as bad fires and good, or prescribed fires. Prescribed fires are used to reduce the build-up of dry wood in forests, preventing potential wildfires. Experienced firefighters ensure that the fire does not spread to areas of human population. Bad fires, on the other hand, are uncontrolled wildfires.

Doctor's Orders!

Wildfires are necessary to maintain the health of forests. Natural fires burn through the forest, consuming dry leaves and branches. Wildfires also encourage better growth of the natural vegetation by destroying unwanted plants, weeds and harmful pests.

Strong, gusty winds can help create a raging, uncontrollable fire disaster.

Wildfires in History

Wildfires can be extremely destructive. Some of the worst wildfires in history have destroyed neighbouring towns and villages, killing thousands of people.

Peshtigo Fire

Considered to be one of the worst wildfires in American history, the Peshtigo Fire occurred on the same day as the Great Chicago Fire of 1871. The summer of 1871, being extremely dry, had witnessed the breakout of several small fires in the forests around Peshtigo. On October 8, strong winds fanned these fires, causing the wildfire to spread to about 12 towns.

European Heat Wave

In 2003, Europe witnessed some of the worst wildfires in its history, when a flaming inferno swept across the continent – from Portugal and Sweden, to east Russia. France and Portugal were the worst hit. More than 22,000 acres of forests were destroyed in the south of France. In Portugal, over 500,000 acres of forests were destroyed in fires.

▼ *A scene of total devastation at San Bernardino County in southern California, following the 2003 forest fires.*

▼ *The more a fire burns, the more fuel it can consume – unless it is brought under control in good time.*

INTERESTING FACT

The Cedar Fire is a classic example of human negligence. It was started by a man named Sergio Martinez, from West Covina, California. Martinez, who was hunting in the area, claimed that he had lost his way and started the fire to capture the attention of rescuers!

FACT FILE

OTHER MAJOR WILDFIRES

- September 5, 1881: Thumb Fire, Michigan, US; over 280 killed and more than a million acres of forest destroyed
- September 1, 1894: Hinckley Fire, Minnesota, US; over 400 killed
- August 20-21, 1910: Great Fire of 1910, Idaho and Montana, US; 86 people killed and over three million acres burned
- September 26, 1970: Laguna Fire in San Diego, California; eight dead and over 175,000 acres of forest destroyed
- July 1988: Yellowstone National Park Fire, US; destroyed about 800,000 acres of the park

▲ *Trees such as the cedar can re-grow after being burned down by a fire, unless the seed is also destroyed.*

Californian Inferno

The fires that raged across southern California in October 2003 were perhaps the worst in the state's history. About 15 fires burned for two weeks in the counties of San Diego, Ventura, Riverside and San Bernardino, killing 24 people and destroying over 800,000 acres of land. The Cedar Fire of San Diego, with the death of 14 people, was the largest in Californian records.

Battling Wildfires

Putting out wildfires not only requires special skills, but also calls for specific equipment. Firefighters wear masks to protect themselves from smoke. Besides the usual hazards, firefighters have to contend with wind speed and direction changes, affecting the fire.

In the Line of Fire

Fire managers first assess the situation and plan a strategy to control the fire. Hotshots are responsible for building fire lines or firebreaks, so the fire does not spread. They remove all flammable material along a strip around the wildfire. The fire is then suppressed by hotshot and engine crews. Helitack crews are trained in the use of helicopters for containing fires. Smokejumpers parachute from planes to fight wildfires in places not otherwise reachable.

Equipment

Water-spraying trucks are the mainstay of ground crews. Crew members use a variety of equipment – from shovels and rakes, to a special tool called a pulaski. A combination of an axe and a mattock, the pulaski can be used to dig soil as well as chop wood. Firefighters wear special fire-resistant clothes to protect themselves from the blaze.

▲ *Firefighters wear masks to protect themselves from smoke.*

▼ *The pulaski is named after its inventor, Ed Pulaski, who was a ranger with the United States Forest Service*

▼ *A tanker truck is about 9 metres (30 feet) long and may hold over 1,000 gallons of water.*

Airborne Fighting

Tanker trucks are inadequate in controlling wildfires since they cannot be driven through dense forests. In such situations, airborne firefighters support the ground crew. The aerial crew use portable water pumps to put out small fires. Both helicopters and fixed-wing aircraft are used in aerial firefighting. Helicopters may be fitted with tanks or carry buckets. The buckets are usually filled by being dipped in local lakes or reservoirs.

▼ *A helicopter spraying water to control a wildfire.*

INTERESTING FACT

The 'backfire' is a method that firefighters may use to control wildfires. Here, a controlled fire is started in the forward path of the fire. The aim is to destroy any flammable material – like dry leaves and twigs – that may lie in the path of the advancing wildfire.

FACT FILE

AIRCRAFT USED IN AERIAL FIREFIGHTING

- Bell UH-1
- Sikorsky Black Hawk
- Thrush Single Engine Aerial Tanker, or SEAT
- S-2 Tracker
- Douglas DC-6 and DC-7
- Martin Mars
- Lockheed C-130 Hercules
- Lockheed P-3 Orion
- IL-76
- Canadair Cl-215 and 217
- Bombardier CL-415
- O-2 Skymaster and OV-10 Bronco
- Beechcraft Baron

Fire Retardants

Apart from water, firefighters also use special chemicals that are capable of slowing down the rate of burning. These chemicals, called retardants, are sprayed over a wildfire to put the flames out.

▼ *A fixed-wing aircraft sprays fire retardant.*

Buildings on Fire

A fire can engulf a building in a short time. If not controlled, not only can a fire destroy a building, it can also spread across the whole neighbourhood and perhaps burn an entire city.

Fire Hazards

The most common cause of fire in buildings is human negligence. Leaving flammable material like wood, paper and aerosol cans near a fireplace or a stove can trigger a fire. Fuel leakage, faulty electrical wiring and cooking accidents are some of the other causes. Many fires have also been started by half-lit cigarettes, candles kept near windows, and children playing with matches.

Risks Galore

Fires in the lower floors of skyscrapers tend to cause the most damage. These fires can spread easily through all levels of the building and block escape routes, like stairwells, and trap the people on the higher floors. That is why skyscrapers are built with many more precautions than required for other buildings.

▲ *A master stream mounted on an aerial ladder can pump out larger quantities of water than a hand-held hose.*

▶ *A firefighter climbs the ladder to attack a fire.*

Fire on the 100th Floor!

Imagine being trapped on the topmost floor of a high-rise building during a fire! Getting out unhurt would prove quite a challenge. Some of the worst high-rise building fires include those at the First Interstate Bank, Los Angeles (1988); One Meridian Plaza, Philadelphia (1991) and World Trade Center in New York (following the 9/11 terrorist attacks in 2001).

Fiery Behaviour

As the fire heats up air in an enclosed area, it causes all combustible material therein to burst into flames in a huge explosion. This is called a flashover. When all the oxygen in the area is used up, the fire begins to die. If, however, there is a fresh supply of oxygen from outside, the fire gases will explode. This is called a backdraft.

▸ *The remains of WTC towers.*

▾ *In high-rise building fires, ladder trucks are used to reach the top floors.*

INTERESTING FACT

Barely an hour after the terrorist attacks on September 11, 2001, the two towers of the World Trade Center (WTC) in New York and a nearby building collapsed. This was the first time that a fire had led to the collapse of a skyscraper. Although there have been other instances of fire in high-rise buildings, never before had a fire caused a steel-framed high-rise building to collapse.

FACT FILE

OTHER BUILDING FIRES

- December 30, 1903: Iroquois Theater, Chicago, US; 602 dead
- December 8, 1881: Ring Theatre, Vienna, Austria; at least 600 dead
- November 28, 1942: Coconut Grove nightclub, Boston, Massachusetts, US; 491 killed
- April 21, 1930: Ohio State Penitentiary, Columbus, Ohio, US; about 320 prisoners killed
- December 5, 1876: Brooklyn Theater, New York City, US; over 300 dead

Safety Precautions

Fire is one of the most common disasters that threatens human lives. Every year, hundreds of people die in fire accidents in buildings. Most countries in the world have now established certain standards that have to be met while constructing homes and Commercial centres.

▲ *A smoke alarm*

Fire Alarms

Every building must have basic fire alarm systems in place. Smoke detectors are the most commonly used alarm systems. A shrill alarm goes off the moment smoke is detected, thus warning people of fire. Smoke detectors have to be tested every month, and batteries have to be changed on a yearly basis. Smoke detectors should also be replaced at least once in 10 years.

▶ *A fire hydrant should be placed at an accessible point in every neighbourhood.*

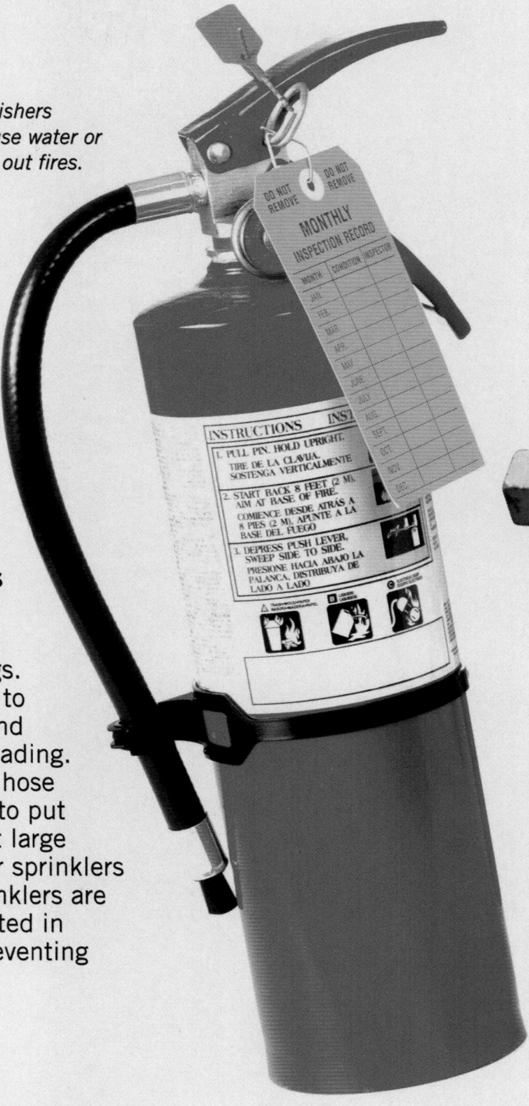

▶ *Fire extinguishers commonly use water or foam to put out fires.*

Fire Extinguishers

Portable fire extinguishers are a must for all buildings. It is the easiest way to control small fires and stop them from spreading. Alternatively, a long hose should be available to put out small fires. Most large buildings have water sprinklers in place. These sprinklers are automatically activated in case of fire, thus preventing it from spreading.

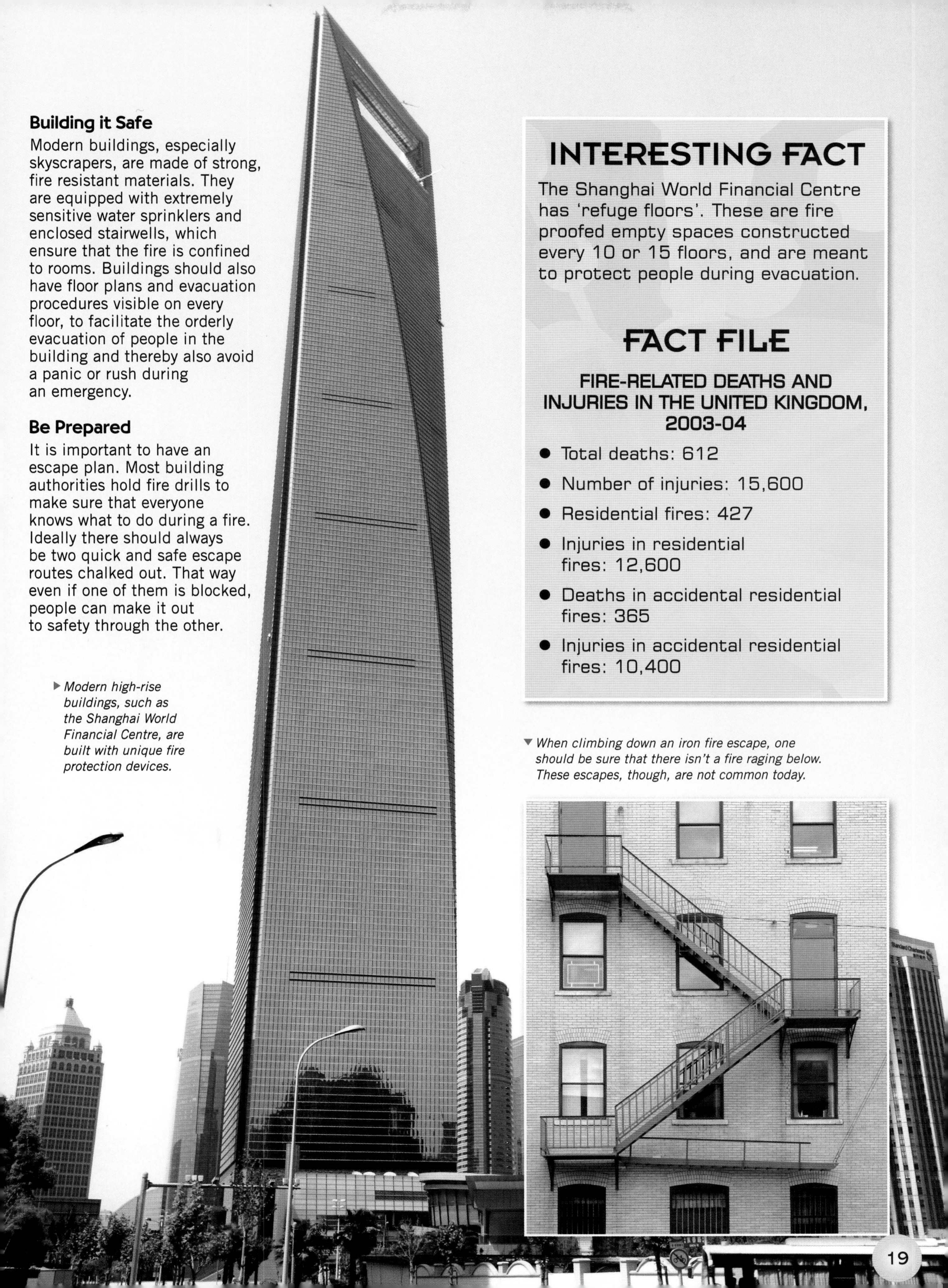

Building it Safe

Modern buildings, especially skyscrapers, are made of strong, fire resistant materials. They are equipped with extremely sensitive water sprinklers and enclosed stairwells, which ensure that the fire is confined to rooms. Buildings should also have floor plans and evacuation procedures visible on every floor, to facilitate the orderly evacuation of people in the building and thereby also avoid a panic or rush during an emergency.

Be Prepared

It is important to have an escape plan. Most building authorities hold fire drills to make sure that everyone knows what to do during a fire. Ideally there should always be two quick and safe escape routes chalked out. That way even if one of them is blocked, people can make it out to safety through the other.

Modern high-rise buildings, such as the Shanghai World Financial Centre, are built with unique fire protection devices.

INTERESTING FACT

The Shanghai World Financial Centre has 'refuge floors'. These are fire proofed empty spaces constructed every 10 or 15 floors, and are meant to protect people during evacuation.

FACT FILE

FIRE-RELATED DEATHS AND INJURIES IN THE UNITED KINGDOM, 2003-04

- Total deaths: 612
- Number of injuries: 15,600
- Residential fires: 427
- Injuries in residential fires: 12,600
- Deaths in accidental residential fires: 365
- Injuries in accidental residential fires: 10,400

When climbing down an iron fire escape, one should be sure that there isn't a fire raging below. These escapes, though, are not common today.

Dos and Don'ts

In case of emergency, there are certain guidelines to be followed. Learning these thoroughly with these will not only ensure your safety, but also help to save others.

- Never ignore a fire alarm. It is always better to be safe than sorry.
- Stay calm and make a quick exit from the building.
- If you are in a high-rise building, exit in an orderly manner. Panic results in a stampede and may cause more fatalities.
- Take the stairs during a fire. You could get trapped in an elevator.
- Stay close to the ground while escaping. Always remember that smoke rises, so you will find cleaner air near the ground.
- Always test a door for heat before opening it. Touch the doorknob with the back of your hand. If it is hot, do not open the door. Look for an alternative route to escape.
- Do not forget to close the door behind once you have exited a room. This helps delay the spread of fire.
- If your clothing catches fire, roll on the ground to put it out.
- Once you have exited the building, call the fire department immediately – in case no one has done so already.

Here are a few things you can do if trapped in a room with no way to escape:

- First seal the opening under the door with wet towels. This will keep the smoke out.
- If there is a phone in the room, call the emergency number or fire department and inform them of your whereabouts.
- Stand near a window and signal for help.
- Do not open the window unless you are sure that there is no fire below it.

INTERESTING FACT

CAUSES OF DOMESTIC FIRES IN ENGLAND AND WALES

- Cooking accidents: 54 percent
- Heating appliances: 9 percent
- Electrical appliances or wiring: 8 percent
- Arson: 5 percent
- Candles: 5 percent
- Matches and cigarettes: 5 percent
- Children playing with fire: 4 percent
- Other causes: 11 percent

▼ *It is particularly crucial to conduct regular fire drills with children, so they are familiar with escape routes during emergencies.*

Call the Fire Department

The fire department consists of dedicated firefighters who take many risks to save thousands of lives. Firefighting involves more than just putting out a fire. It also includes assessing the nature of the fire, the kind of fuel involved, and finding and rescuing people.

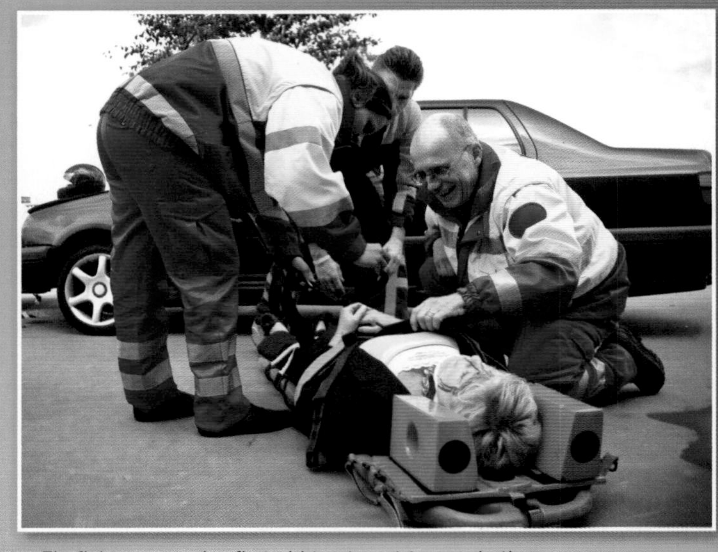

▲ *Firefighters can give first-aid treatment to people they rescue.*

To the Rescue

When firefighters arrive at the scene, they make a quick assessment of the situation and proceed to evacuate people from the building or area. Sometimes they have to locate trapped people or animals. Firefighters work in teams. They wear fire-resistant clothes and breathing masks to safeguard against smoke and other poisonous gases.

Fighting with Water

Water is most commonly used to put out fires. Wetting agents called detergents help water to penetrate objects such as mattresses. But flammable liquids like oil and petroleum float on water and help fire spread easily. In these situations, the fire is put out using foam.

▼ *A firefighter sprays water to douse the flames.*

Tools of Life

Fire vehicles include tankers, pumpers and ladder trucks. Tankers can carry more water than pumpers. Ladder trucks have long ladders that help firefighters reach the upper floors of tall buildings. Equipment such as ropes, axes and hoses are commonly used. Firefighters also carry extrication tools like spreaders and cutters to free trapped people.

▲ *Fire engines are equipped with various tools such as hoses, ladders and pike poles, as well as a water tank.*

Forever on Call

Firefighters also play an important role when other natural disasters like floods and earthquakes strike. They help during road and rail accidents, and plane crashes as well.

INTERESTING FACT

Most firefighters carry a Personal Alert Safety System (PASS) when entering a building. This is a one way communication device that alerts the Rapid Entry Team on standby outside, in case the wearer gets into trouble and has to be rescued.

FACT FILE

U.K. FIRE STATISTICS, 2003-04

- Total fires reported: 1,061,400
- Actual fires attended: 592,300
- False alarms: 469,100
- Outdoor fires: 375,200
- Property fires: 206,600
- Building fires: 104,500
- Vehicle fires: 88,300
- Residential fires: 63,200
- Fires in Commercial premises and schools: 41,300

▼ *Firefighters at the scene of a motor vehicle accident.*

Towns on Fire

Sometimes, a small fire that starts in a house or a barn progresses to burn down an entire city. Many such instances of a fire destroying a city, are recorded in history.

Great Fire of London

The Great Fire of 1666 destroyed almost every public building in London. The fire broke out at the house of Thomas Farriner, a baker to King Charles II. It is said that Farriner forgot to put out his oven before going to bed. Sometime later, the embers from the oven set fire to some nearby wood. Aided by a strong wind, the fire spread across the neighbourhood.

The present St Paul's Cathedral in London was designed by architect Christopher Wren after the original one was burned in the 1666 fire.

Great Chicago Fire

According to a popular legend, the fire that devastated Chicago in 1871 started in a barn owned by Kate O'Leary, when her cow kicked over a lantern. However, it is now believed that the fire was started by Daniel Sullivan, who had first reported it. Sullivan is said to have accidentally knocked over the lantern while trying to steal milk from Mrs. O'Leary's barn.

The Great Chicago Fire of 1871 is believed to have started in a barn.

Fire in San Francisco

Soon after a devastating earthquake rocked San Francisco on the morning of April 18, 1906, over 50 separate fires broke out. The quake had led to leaks from the main gas lines, causing the flare-ups. The fires were finally controlled, by dynamiting buildings to create firebreaks.

▲ *A view of the fire that raged through San Francisco following the earthquake of 1906.*

Tokyo in Flames

On September 1, 1923, an earthquake measuring 7.9 on the Richter scale struck the Japanese island of Honshu. The quake destroyed Yokohama, a port city, along with the surrounding areas of Chiba, Kanagawa, Shizuoka and Tokyo. Most of the 105,000 deaths were caused by 88 fires that broke out after the quake.

▼ *Tokyo was completely devastated by the Great Kanto Earthquake and the ensuing fire.*

INTERESTING FACT

At the same time that Chicago burned, two other major fires erupted in the states of Wisconsin and Michigan. This strange occurrence gave birth to several theories. According to one of the weirdest, the fires in the three states were probably caused by fragments of Biela's Comet crashing into the Earth's atmosphere.

FACT FILE

OTHER MAJOR TOWN FIRES

- 1204: Constantinople burns thrice during the Fourth Crusade (war fought to capture the Holy Land of Jerusalem from the Muslims)
- 1702: Fire in Uppsala, Sweden, destroys a major part of the city, including the cathedral and Uppsala Castle
- 1889: The Great Fire of Seattle devastates the entire city. All railroad terminals and most of the wharves are destroyed. Fortunately, no one is killed
- 1947: Texas City Disaster; two ships carrying ammonium nitrate explode, causing massive destruction to the port and killing over 450 people with another 100 declared as 'missing'

Fire Timeline

Despite the fact that fire can be a useful tool, we are often rendered helpless in the face of a raging blaze. History is full of incidents in which fires have engulfed buildings and cities.

History in Flames

Some of the biggest building fires occurred during ancient times. Most of these disasters were caused by humans. The famed Temple of Artemis at Ephesus, in modern-day Turkey, was one such casualty. Dedicated to Artemis, the Greek goddess of hunting, the temple was one of the Seven Wonders of the World. On the night of July 21, 356 BC, a young Greek named Herostratus set fire to the temple. Legend has it that Herostratus committed the crime to become famous.

Great Fire of Rome

On July 18, AD 64, a conflagration engulfed the city of Rome. The fire started among a few clustered shops and spread quickly through the streets. More than half the city was destroyed. Emperor Nero, the ruler of Rome at the time, was not in the city during the fire – giving rise to the famous rumour that Nero 'played the fiddle' while he watched Rome burn.

In 1991, following the Persian Gulf War, the defeated Iraqi armed forces set fire to several of Kuwait's oil wells before retreating. The fires burned for several months.

The Halifax Explosion

On December 6, 1917, a French ship, Mont Blanc, and a Norwegian ship, Imo, collided in the harbour near Halifax, Nova Scotia, Canada. A fire started on-board the Mont Blanc, which was carrying a huge amount of ammunitions to Europe during World War I. A few minutes later, a massive explosion took place, killing more than 1,600 people. About half of the town was wiped out.

It was Publius Cornelius Tacitus, the Roman historian, who started the rumour that Nero 'played the fiddle' as he watched Rome burn

The Atomic Bomb

On August 6, 1945, the first atomic bomb was dropped on the unsuspecting people of Hiroshima, Japan. Over 70,000 people were killed outright or shortly after the blast. A firestorm swept through the city immediately after, claiming more lives. Three days later, the second atomic bomb was dropped on Japan – this time on Nagasaki. About 40,000 people were reported to have died almost instantly. Several fires broke out, burning down houses and commercial buildings.

The 1945 atomic bombing produced a mushroom-like cloud formation over Hiroshima and Nagasaki.

INTERESTING FACT

The Great Library of Alexandria in Egypt was destroyed by fire. In AD 272, Roman Emperor Aurelian had the main quarter of the library burned down. The complete destruction took place in AD 640, when Arabs captured the city of Alexandria.

FACT FILE

FIREFIGHTING LANDMARKS

- AD 6: Roman fire brigade formed by Emperor Augustus
- 1648: Fire wardens appointed in New York, US.
- 1672: Fire hose invented by Dutch inventor Jan Van der Heiden
- 1725: Fire engine developed by Richard Newsham, a pearl button maker from London
- 1810: The first 'professional' firefighters, called Sapeurs-Pompiers, are created in France by Emperor Napoleon Bonaparte
- 1824: The Edinburgh Fire Engine Establishment, credited as the first organised firefighting company in the United Kingdom, is formed in Edinburgh, Scotland

River Floods

Like fire, water also has the power to destroy lives and property. When water levels rise faster than the ground can absorb it, flooding occurs. Floods can sweep away houses, trees and cars, and even drown people.

Causes

Floods can be caused by heavy rains, melting snow, broken dams, hurricanes and underwater volcanic eruptions. Broadly speaking, floods are of two kinds – regular river or coastal floods, and flash floods.

The River Overflows

River floods are caused when rivers overflow. This can happen due to several reasons. Heavy rains, either seasonal or caused by severe storms, can fill rivers and streams with more water than they can hold. When this happens, the water flows over the banks. Continuous rainfall can eventually cause water levels to rise and lead to flooding.

◀ *An overflowing river causes floods.*

▲ *Torrential rains are one of the major causes of floods.*

Killer Rivers

The largest river floods have been recorded in China, where the Yangtze River has flooded almost every second year in the last 2,000 years. But it is the Hwang Ho (Yellow River) – also dubbed as 'China's Sorrow' – that has been responsible for more deaths than any other river in the world. The 1887 floods alone killed almost two million people.

▲ *A vehicle submerged in swelling waters.*

Gift of the Nile

Not all river floods are destructive. For thousands of years, the Egyptians benefited from the flooding of the Nile. Every summer, when the mountain snow melted, the Nile flooded its banks – leaving behind deposits of black soil suitable for agriculture.

▼ *The soil deposited by the river Nile was very fertile. Hence, the annual flooding of the river was called the 'Gift of the Nile'!*

INTERESTING FACT

In 1970, the Aswan High Dam was built across the Nile to stop the river's annual flooding, so that farmers could plant crops throughout the year. Unfortunately, though, the dam has also prevented rich soil from being deposited on the riverbanks. As a result, farmers have had to resort to artificial fertilisers.

FACT FILE

OTHER MAJOR FLOODS

- 1931: Hwang Ho; 850,000-4,000,000 people dead
- 1953: North Sea; about 2,000 dead in the Netherlands and the United Kingdom
- 1975: Typhoon strikes Henan Province in China, destroying more than 60 dams and causing floods; over 200,000 killed
- 2000: Mozambique flood; thousands killed and millions rendered homeless
- 2002: European flood; also called the 'flood of the century', it engulfs several countries including Russia, Germany, Poland and the Czech Republic; over 100 people killed

Wrath of the Sea

Sometimes storms lead to a lot of water rushing onto coastal areas - these are called storm surges. Low-lying coastal areas are most vulnerable to storm surges.

▼ *The strong, whirling winds of a hurricane can cause huge waves in sea waters and flood coastal areas*

When the Wind Blows

One of the most common factors that affect sea levels is a hurricane. The storm makes the ocean surface fiercer than usual. Strong winds can create monstrous waves that crash onto the beach, destroying houses and sometimes killing people. Storm surges are intensified by high tide and the direction in which the wind blows.

Hurricane Menace

The worst storm surges in history have occurred in Bangladesh. In 1970, about 500,000 people were killed in a cyclone and accompanying storm surge. In 1991, about half of the country was flooded and over 139,000 killed in a devastating cyclone followed by huge storm surges.

▼ *People in Bangladesh brave the flood waters to crowd outside a relief camp for food.*

Killer Waves

Underwater volcanoes and earthquakes can create giant waves that are capable of travelling long distances at very high speeds. These waves, called tsunamis, can be more than 15 metres (50 feet) high and cause heavy destruction when they crash against the coast. The force of these killer waves can sweep away people, vehicles and even buildings.

▶ *Tsunamis are very powerful waves and can cause extensive damage.*

▲ *A scene of the devastating Asian tsunami as it strikes the coast of Sri Lanka.*

Asian Tragedy

On December 26, 2004, an underwater earthquake occurred near the Indonesian island of Sumatra. The event generated a tsunami that went on to wreak havoc across eight countries, with over 10 others suffering various extents of damage. The most affected were Indonesia, Sri Lanka, South India and Thailand. The effects of the killer waves were felt as far as Port Elizabeth in South Africa. About 300,000 people have been reported dead.

INTERESTING FACT

The word 'tsunami' means 'harbour wave' in Japanese. A tsunami is often incorrectly referred to as a tidal wave. It is not caused by tides, but is actually a result of seismic activity on the ocean floor.

FACT FILE

WORST TSUNAMIS IN HISTORY

- November 1, 1755: Three tsunamis strike the coast of Lisbon in Portugal, in the wake of an earthquake; about 30,000 are killed; the effect is felt in Britain, Spain, Morocco and even as far away as the West Indies
- August 27, 1883: Krakatoa, Indonesia; a tsunami caused by volcanic eruption kills over 36,000 people

Flash Floods

Flash floods are sudden and unexpected surges of water, which makes them faster and more dangerous than normal floods. Like normal floods, though, flash floods are caused by tropical storms, dam failures, heavy rains and rapid melting of snow.

Melting Glaciers

When snow in nearby mountains starts melting at a very fast pace, it can lead to flash floods. Heat waves are usually the reason for rapid melting of snow. The water fills the streams, which are unable to hold the excess water, causing floods.

When a Dam Breaks

A breach in a dam is usually unpredictable and can happen within minutes. This lets out huge amounts of water, which surges downstream causing immense destruction. Reasons for a dam failure can be poor design, bad construction, poor maintenance, or damage caused by natural disasters like earthquakes.

▲ *The tremendous volume and flow of water released by a dam break can cause much damage.*

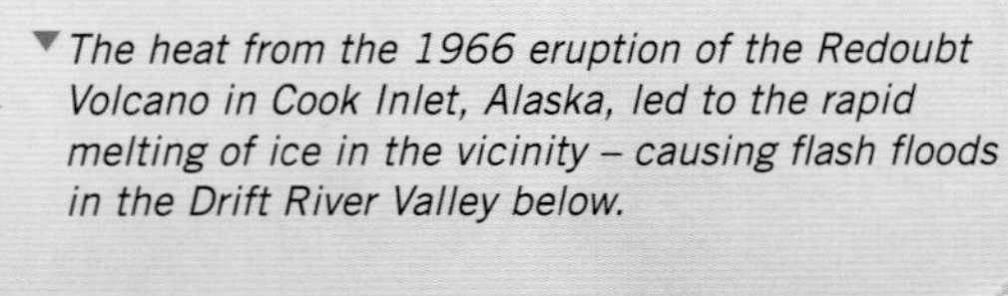

▼ *The heat from the 1966 eruption of the Redoubt Volcano in Cook Inlet, Alaska, led to the rapid melting of ice in the vicinity – causing flash floods in the Drift River Valley below.*

▲ *The 1977 flash flood at Kaiparowits Coal Basin, Utah, was caused by rains that fell on Fifty-Mile Mountain about 109 km (68 miles) away!*

Surging Downhill

Flash floods are considered to be more dangerous than normal floods because they are unpredictable. The water keeps moving as long as there is a path downhill. Flash floods are also strong enough to sweep away vehicles and houses. A large majority of people who die during flooding are victims of flash floods.

The Human Effect

Huge numbers of trees are cut down around the world for various reasons. This has lead to a decrease in forest cover. Without enough trees and plants to hold back the water flow, floods are becoming more and more destructive. Global warming is responsible for heat waves and the rapid melting of snow, thus increasing the likelihood of floods.

◀ *Forests are destroyed to build new roads, houses and other establishments.*

INTERESTING FACT

The disappearance of wetlands is also contributing to flood damage. Wetlands are swampy lands along the banks of rivers such as the Mississippi. The wet soil in these regions usually soaks up a lot of water. However, these wetlands are now being replaced with farms and houses, increasing the chance of floods.

FACT FILE

MAJOR FLASH FLOOD INCIDENTS

- May 31, 1889: Johnstown, Pennsylvania, US; caused by breaking of the South Fork Dam; over 2,200 casualties
- August 1954: Teheran, Iran; water flooded a street, killing 2,000 people who had gathered for prayers
- July 31, 1976: Big Thompson Canyon, Loveland, Colorado, US; about 140 persons killed

Flood Control

A common way to control floods is by building dams across rivers. A chief factor for flooding today, is the effect of human activity on the environment. Planting trees will prevent soil erosion and in turn help contain floods. Preserving wetlands is another option.

Putting up Barriers

For years now, huge, sturdy dams have been constructed across rivers to control flooding. A reservoir, or artificial lake, constructed behind the dam stores the water, which is then supplied for irrigation and also used to produce electricity. Canals are dug to drain excess water.

▲ *The Thames Barrier has been raised more than 70 times since its construction was completed in 1982.*

Keeping the Sea Out

There is not much that man can do to stop a raging sea from destroying the shores. However, coastal defences like sea walls, dikes and beach nourishment help reduce the extent of damage. Sea walls are constructed on the coast to reduce the effect of strong waves. Beach nourishment is the process by which sand lost by erosion is replaced.

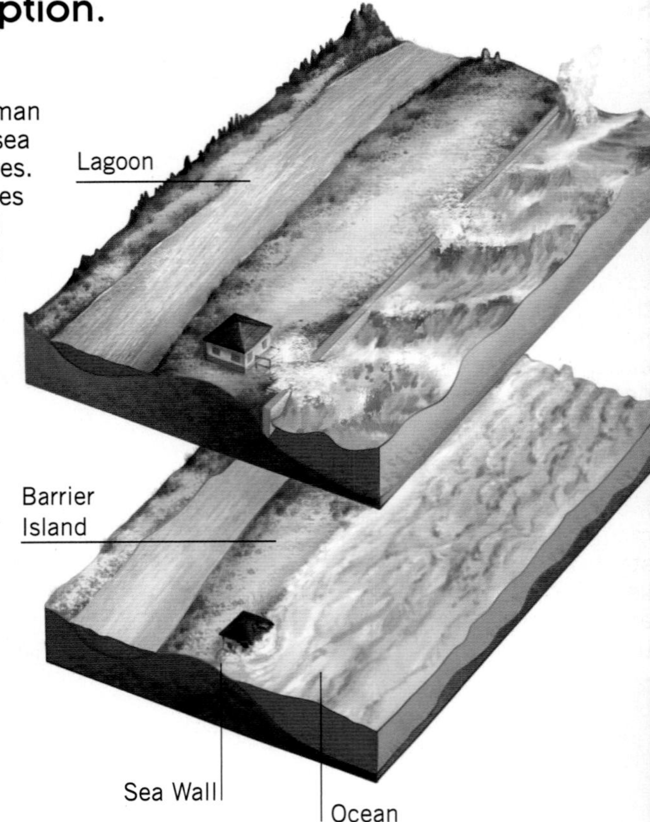

▶ *Sea walls are usually made of concrete and may be vertical, sloping or curved.*

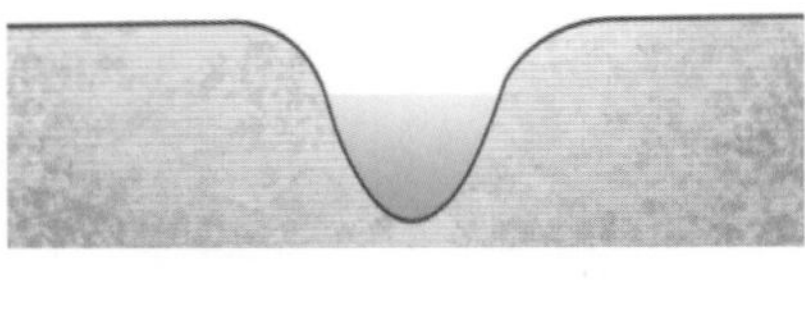

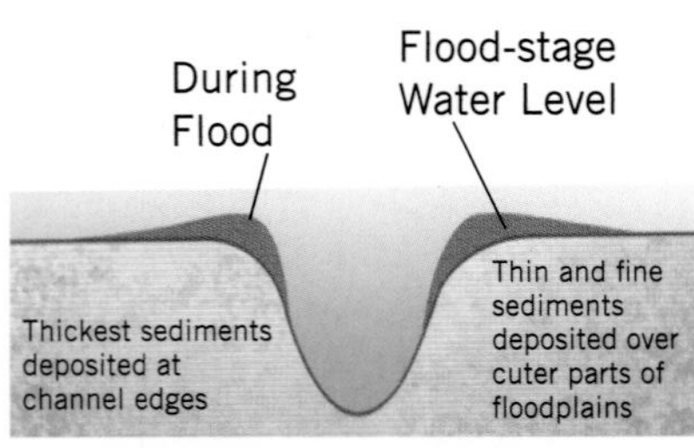

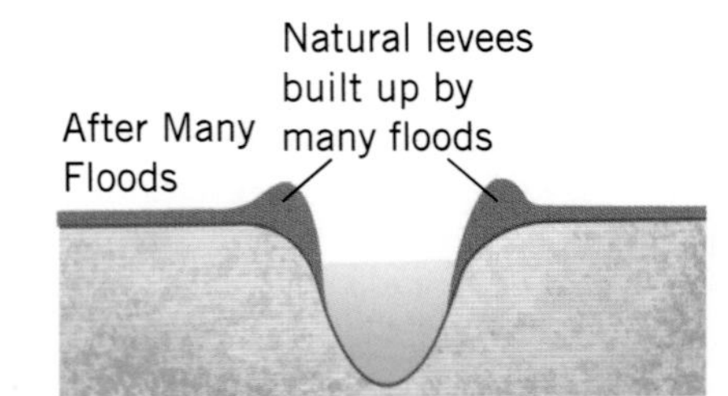

Levees

Apart from dams, levees and dikes are also used to prevent overflowing river water. A levee is a slope that runs along a riverbank. It can be natural or man-made. Man-made levees are usually built by piling up mud from the bank. They are broad at the base and taper towards the top.

Dikes

Dikes are walls made of stone or baked clay built to defend an area from floods. Dikes can be permanent structures or just built during a flood emergency. They are also built to reclaim land from the sea. Series of dikes can be built to keep the sea out and create new land by draining the water away.

▶ *Planting trees will prevent soil erosion, thus reducing the chances and effects of floods.*

lood Forecast

Unlike fire, floods are definitely more predictable. Over the years, early warning systems and flood forecasts have helped save many lives.

▲ *TIROS I was successfully used to survey atmospheric conditions from space.*

Eyes in the Sky

Weather satellites gather vital information and capture pictures of cloud formations from above the Earth. These pictures help predict thunderstorms, hurricanes and even flash floods. After the scientists collect enough data, it is communicated to people through television, radio and online.

Monitoring Water Levels

Most developed countries have river-monitoring and rainfall-measuring stations. Scientists in these stations keep a close watch on water levels and the amount of rain received in the region.

▲ *The water levels and the flow of river water are monitored by gauging stations like this.*

Preparing for the Flood

The moment a warning is given, turn off the main power supply and prepare to evacuate. If time is short for evacuation, move to higher ground. Avoid wading into floodwaters, since they are highly infectious and can spread diseases. Listen to the radio continuously for updates.

Gauging Floods

Rain gauges are used to measure the amount of rainfall in a particular area. Scientists also use flow measuring equipment to monitor the speed of a river flow. Coastal flooding predictions are made in similar fashion to ones for river floods and flash floods. Special ocean monitoring stations and tsunami warning centres have also been set up to forewarn people in coastal areas.

▲ *The markings on river stakes are monitored for rising water levels.*

▼ *Always heed road signs and avoid storm drains. Also, keep away from blocked roads.*

INTERESTING FACT

The first weather satellite, Vanguard 2, was launched on February 17, 1959. Unfortunately, it was a failure. It was only on April 1, 1960, that the US-based National Aeronautics and Space Administration (NASA) launched the first successful weather satellite – TIROS-1.

FACT FILE

OPERATIONAL WEATHER SATELLITES

United States

- Geostationary Operational Environmental Satellite- (GOES-)9; monitors the mid-Pacific region
- GOES-10; covers the eastern Pacific Ocean
- GOES-12; over the Amazon River; provides most of the weather information on the United States and Europe
- METEOSAT-5; monitors the Indian Ocean region
- METEOSAT-6, 7 and 8; cover the Atlantic Ocean and Russia
- GOMS; operated over the Equator south of the Russian capital, Moscow

To the Rescue

The extent and focus of rescue and relief efforts depends upon the type of flood. During flash floods, the emphasis is on saving lives; while in slow-moving river floods, preventing damage to property gains importance.

A Tough Battle

The members of a rescue team undergo strict training in water rescue, especially swift-water rescue. This comes in handy particularly during flash floods.

Tools for Rescue

Boats are one of the most important tools of flood rescue. They are the only means of transportation during floods and, hence, are vital to rescue work. Flotation devices, ropes and safety lines come in very handy in rescue efforts. Rescuers wear helmets to protect their heads from rocks and logs that are swept along by the water. Sometimes, land rescuers are aided by helicopters and army personnel.

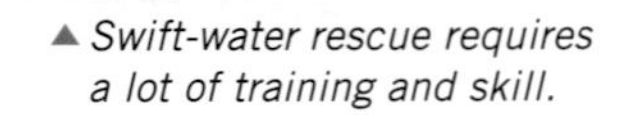

▲ *Swift-water rescue requires a lot of training and skill.*

▼ *The local police are patrolling a flood-hit area. The local police and firefighters are usually the first to arrive at a flood scene.*

Life After the Flood

The rushing water can deposit a huge amount of mud, capable of burying everything. Houses can be swept away. Railroads, bridges and highways can be broken or washed away. Telephone lines can be destroyed, making communication impossible. Imagine having to rebuild after such an enormous loss. This is what people who live in flood-prone areas do every time a flood washes their homes away.

▲ *In emergencies, helicopters are used to airlift people marooned by the rising flood waters.*

The Aftermath

Some of the worst effects of floods are felt after the water has receded. This is because floods are capable of spreading diseases. More people die due to epidemics that spread after a flood, so medical aid is of utmost importance. Floods also destroy crops, leading to starvation and poverty. In 1887, more than one million Chinese starved to death after a flood destroyed their crops.

▶ *Relief measures in flood-affected areas include the supply of food and medicines.*

Myths and Legends

Ancient people considered fire and flood disasters to be an expression of the anger of gods or Mother Nature. In many countries, people made human and animal sacrifices to appease the elements.

Discovery of Fire

According to a Greek legend, Prometheus, who created man, wanted to gift his creation the warmth of fire. He went to Zeus with his request. Although Zeus turned him down, Prometheus was determined, so he stole fire from the gods and gave it to mankind.

Zeus punished Prometheus, who had stolen fire, by chaining him to the Caucasus Mountain

Fire Gods

In many countries, fire gods are much feared and often, disasters are attributed to their anger. This is most pronounced in Hawaii. According to the local legend, Pele, the goddess of fire, resides on Mauna Kea. She is regarded as the protector of the Hawaiian people, but at the same time, she is feared for her violent temper. In Greek mythology, Hephaestus is worshipped as the god of fire, while Vulcan is the Roman equivalent of Hephaestus. In India, fire continues to be an important part of rituals in the Hindu religion.

Legends of the Floods

Like fire, floods also have been the focus of various legends. According to a Chinese story, Great Yu, a Chinese emperor, is said to have tamed floods by diverting the river's course. It took him 13 years to cut channels for this purpose.

The ancient Chinese attributed fire and flood to an angry dragon.

Hawaiian people attribute volcanic eruptions to Goddess Pele's anger.

INTERESTING FACT

According to a Cherokee legend, lightning buried fire in a tree trunk. Several animals tried to get the fire. However, only a water spider succeeded. The spider spun a bowl of web, in which she carried a piece of coal from the fire and gifted it to mankind.

FACT FILE

- Circa 5 million years ago the Mediterranean Sea flooded. Prior to that, the sea had dried up after the natural blocking of the Strait of Gibraltar
- Circa 5600 BC: Black Sea flooded due to rise in the water levels of the Mediterranean
- 15,000-13,000 years ago: Missoula Floods; the periodic floods caused by rupture of ice dams across the Glacial Lake Missoula in Montana, US.

The Great Deluge

Most cultures in the world talk about a 'great deluge' that destroyed mankind. The Holy Bible refers to a great flood that was sent by God to destroy evil on Earth. An honest man named Noah and his family were the only ones to survive the terrible flood. Similar references can be seen in Greek, Roman, Indian, Chinese and Scandinavian mythology.

According to the Bible, before the 'great deluge', Noah built a huge ark in which he sheltered one male and female each of every animal.

Atmosphere

The Earth is surrounded by a thin blanket of air called the atmosphere, which is held in place by gravity. The atmosphere absorbs and reflects the Sun's energy, so preventing too much heat from entering the Earth. It also recycles water.

Weather

Weather is the state of the Earth's atmosphere at a particular time over a particular place. It occurs because the atmosphere is forever changing. Factors that influence weather include temperature, air pressure, wind, clouds and precipitation.

Pollution from industries and vehicles is causing a rise in the Earth's temperature. This phenomenon of global warming is affecting weather patterns drastically, causing excessive floods, drought and heat waves.

LAYERS OF THE ATMOSPHERE

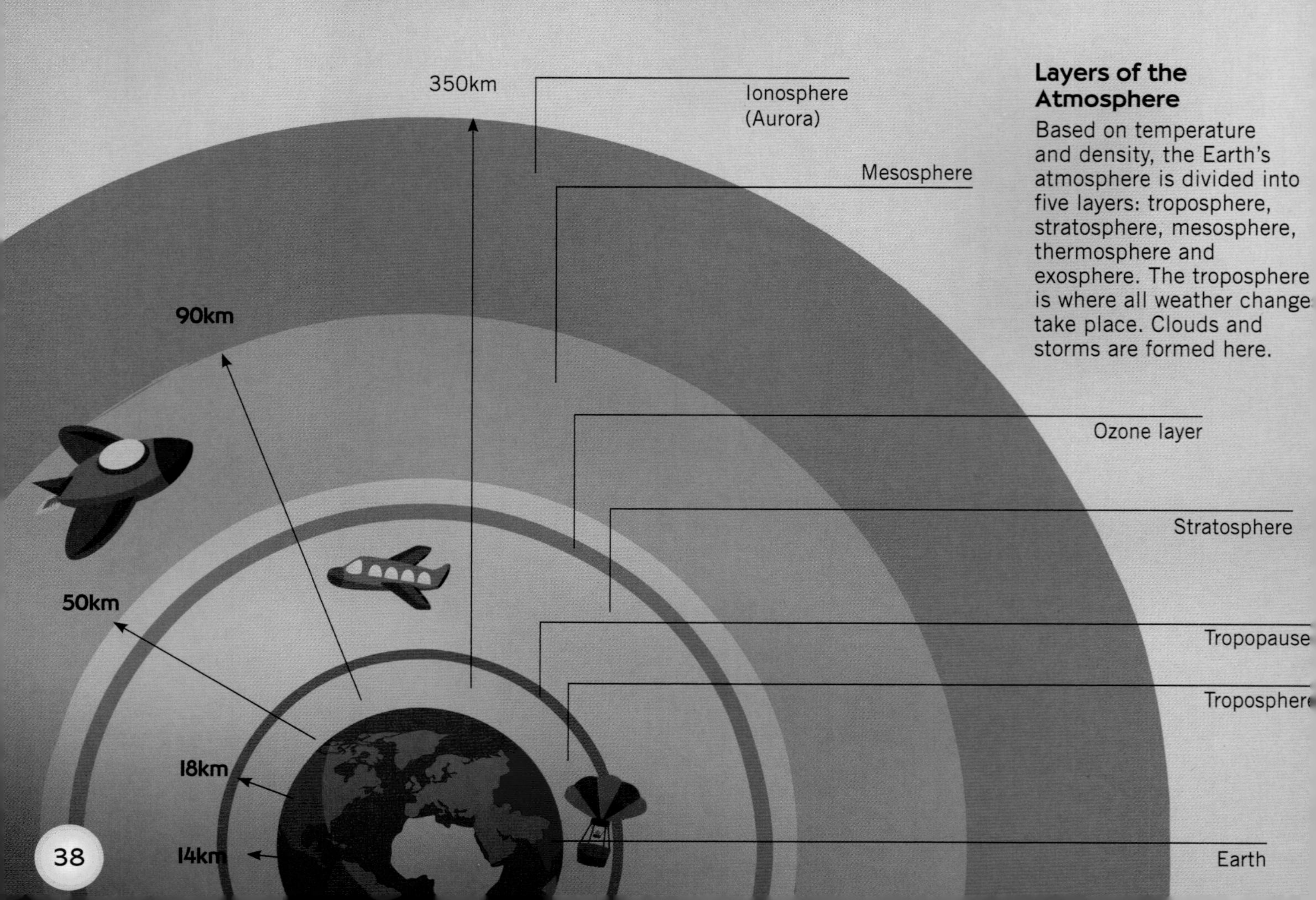

Layers of the Atmosphere

Based on temperature and density, the Earth's atmosphere is divided into five layers: troposphere, stratosphere, mesosphere, thermosphere and exosphere. The troposphere is where all weather change take place. Clouds and storms are formed here.

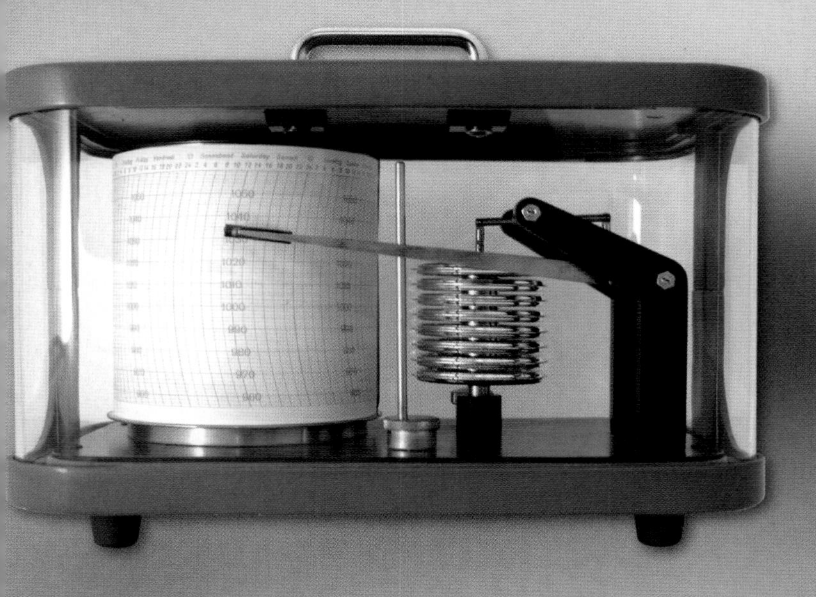

▲ *An aneroid barograph records changes in the atmospheric pressure.*

Air Pressure

The air molecules in the atmosphere exert weight on the surroundings. This weight is known as pressure and it depends on the amount of molecules present and their speed. As we go up, the number of molecules decrease, thus reducing the pressure. Air pressure also changes with the temperature. A rise in temperature will usually lower the air pressure.

Air Mass

A large body of air that exhibits uniform temperature and humidity is called an air mass. The property of an air mass depends on the source region. An air mass over polar regions is normally cold and dry. When an air mass moves from the source region, it will meet another mass with different properties.

▶ *The boundary between two air masses is called a front. Cold fronts are responsible for stormy weather*

INTERESTING FACT

All living things need oxygen to breathe. However, oxygen makes up only 21 percent of the Earth's atmosphere. The atmosphere mainly consists of nitrogen, which accounts for about 78 percent of the total gas present in the atmosphere!

FACT FILE

REGIONS OF THE ATMOSPHERE

- Troposphere: About 10-13 km (6-8 miles) above the Earth's surface
- Stratosphere: From a lower boundary of about 6-17 km (4-11 miles) to a higher boundary at about 50 km (30 miles)
- Mesosphere: Between about 50 km (30 miles) and 80 km (50 miles)
- Thermosphere: Between about 80 km (50 miles) and 450 km (280 miles)
- Exosphere: Begins at an altitude of about 500 km (300 miles)

The Weather Goes Wild

Blizzards, thunderstorms, hurricanes, heat waves, droughts and hailstorms are some examples of extreme or severe weather conditions. We are all fascinated and also a little scared when the weather goes wild. Extreme weather events can damage property and crops, and even endanger our lives.

When the negatively charged particles in a thunderstorm meet the positively charged particles on the ground, a channel is formed. Electric current passing through this channel forces air molecules to release light. This is how lightning occurs.

Unpredictable Weather

The atmosphere is in constant motion, making the weather largely unpredictable. As well as temperature, precipitation (rain, snow, or hail), wind speed and atmospheric pressure, the Earth's tilt as it revolves around the Sun also causes changes in the weather. The study of weather is known as meteorology and scientists who study and predict weather are called meteorologists.

The water droplets on the top of thunderstorm clouds freeze to form ice crystals. Sometimes, these ice crystals melt to fall down as rain. At other times, they grow in size and come down as hailstones.

Winter Storms

Winter storms may bring snow, freezing rain or sleet, and ice. They include blizzards, ice storms and 'nor'easters' (strong northeasterly winds). Winter storms often create havoc, disrupting normal life and activities. Heavy snowfall can reduce visibility, making driving during snowstorms dangerous.

Blizzards are severe snowstorms accompanied by strong winds. People and animals can get buried in snow during blizzards.

Thunderstorm

A thunderstorm includes thunder and lightning, and usually rain or hail. Most thunderstorms are not destructive, however, severe ones can lead to floods or cause fires. Sometimes, thunderstorms can even produce tornadoes. Thunderstorms usually occur during spring and summer. Most of these violent storms strike in the afternoon or evening.

◄ *The humidity in rising warm air condenses to form clouds, ice crystals and rain, resulting in a thunderstorm. However, upper-air disturbances, which are pools of cold air moving along with the winds, may provide a lifting motion to produce an unusually strong thunderstorm.*

INTERESTING FACT

In 1993, from March 12 to 15, an unusually powerful 'nor'easter' produced a trail of snow, flood and hurricane-force winds in the eastern United States. From Alabama to Maine, it was a time of record breaking cold temperatures. Florida was hit by tornadoes. In all, over 235 people died and damage worth more than $1 billion was caused. The storm earned the epithet "Storm of the Century"!

FACT FILE

Meteorologists define weather as 'severe' when one of the following things happens:

- Hail 2 cm in diameter, or larger;
- Wind gusts 25 metres per second (58 miles per hour), or more;
- Wind causes damage such as the uprooting of trees and the destruction of homes and buildings;
- A storm occurs

Heat Wave

'Heat wave' is a term used to describe extraordinarily hot weather over a long period. One of the main causes of heat waves is global warming - excessive heating of the Earth's surface. Heat waves can cause heat strokes, which can be fatal. Sometimes heat waves are accompanied by a drought.

Watching the Wind

Wind refers to the movement of air over the Earth's surface. It is usually caused by differences in temperature and pressure due to the unequal heating of the Earth's surface. When the Sun heats up a certain area, the air above that place is also heated. The warm air rises, and cool air comes in to take its place. This movement creates winds.

Winds are caused by the Earth's rotation and differences in atmospheric pressure. Wind always flows from a point of high pressure to a point of low pressure.

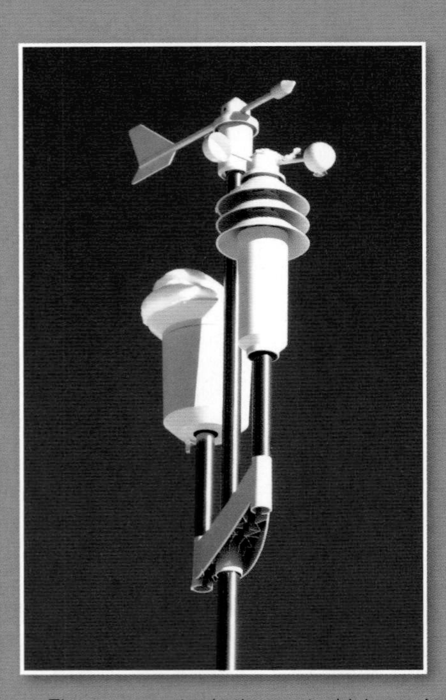

The anemometer is the most widely used instrument for measuring wind speeds.

Measuring the Wind

Meteorologists use various instruments to study wind and measure its speed, direction, temperature and pressure. Surface winds are measured by weather vanes and anemometers. Winds higher up in the atmosphere are studied using pilot balloons or aircraft reports.

Beaufort Wind Scale

Sir Francis Beaufort (1777-1857) of the British Royal Navy devised a system of estimating wind speeds. The Beaufort force or number combines the wind speed with the visible effects of the wind on land objects and/or sea surfaces. The numbers range from 0 to 12, going from calm air and breeze to strong winds or gales.

Coriolis Effect

As the Earth spins, winds tend to move to the right in the Northern Hemisphere, and to the left in the Southern Hemisphere. This movement of winds is called the Coriolis effect. It has a great influence on weather patterns.

Weather vanes on top of barns and houses tell us in which direction the wind is blowing.

Going in Different Directions

Winds are also classified according to the direction from which they blow. Easterly winds blow from east to west, while the westerly ones blow from west to east. Trade winds are steady and flow towards the Equator.

Strong winds blowing over dry land can cause dust storms.

Wind and sand erosion have curved the splendid sandstone rocks in Utah, US.

INTERESTING FACT

Air from high-pressure areas flows towards low-pressure areas. Since the pressure can change quickly, the air travels at high speeds between areas of different pressures, forming strong winds. These winds, which can reach speeds of over 320 kilometres per hour (199 mph), are called jet streams.

FACT FILE

BEAUFORT SCALE NUMBER	DESCRIPTIVE TERM
0	Calm
1-3	Light Winds
4	Moderate Winds
5	Fresh Winds
6	Strong Winds
7	Near Gale
8	Gale
9	Strong Gale
10	Storm
11	Violent Storm
12+	Hurricane

Weather at Sea

Sailors often face dangerous and life-threatening weather at sea. They must cope with tidal waves, tsunamis and tropical storms. The effects of such severe weather conditions are also felt on land, where immense loss of life and property can occur.

▲ *Tidal waves are not destructive like 'free waves', but one must keep away from beaches, coves and sea caves during high tides since the chances of drowning are higher.*

Tidal Wave

A tidal wave is a sea wave caused by tidal forces. It is usually used to refer to the huge swelling of the ocean surface on either side of the Earth. It is caused by the gravitational forces of the Sun and the Moon, and not by earthquakes – as many people wrongly believe. The wave produced by an earthquake is called a 'free wave'.

Tsunami

A tsunami (from the Japanese 'tsu' for 'harbour' and 'nami' for 'wave') is a large, destructive wave. It is very different from a tidal wave. A tsunami may be caused by earthquakes, submarine landslides, volcanic eruptions and even meteorite strikes. As the wave heads toward the shore, it gains height and speed. By the time it hits the shore, the tsunami may have a 30 metre (100 feet) tall crest.

▲ *A tsunami travels outward from its starting point – much like the ripples in a pond, until it hits the shore.*

Tropical Storms

A tropical cyclone is a violent, tropical weather system in which the air in the centre is warmer than the surrounding winds. These storms go through many stages as they develop, and each has a life span of several days. They are accompanied by very heavy rain, thunder and lightning.

◀ *Lighthouses warn ships of dangers like rocks and low water levels. They also help to show the way during storms and heavy rains.*

▼ *Anchored buoys are used for weather observation at sea. Each buoy is equipped with instruments that record and monitor weather developments.*

INTERESTING FACT

The tsunami that hit the southeast and south Asian countries around the Indian Ocean on December 26, 2004, was generated by an earthquake measuring 9.2 on the Richter scale. It literally shook the world. A NASA geophysicist reported that the planet tilted about 2.5 cm (0.9 inches) on its axis and spun three microseconds faster.

FACT FILE

A TSUNAMI CAN

- Travel as quickly as a jet plane (more than 640 kph or 400 mph)
- Travel unobserved on the surface of deep seas, at speeds up to 800 kph or 500 mph
- Have a wavelength of up to 1000 km, or 600 miles
- Comprise a set of waves that may last for several hours
- Be as high as 30 metres (100 feet)

MOST ACTIVE TSUNAMI ZONE

- The Pacific

Here Comes the Hurricane

Hurricanes are large, rotating storms that form over warm oceans near the Equator. These tropical storms may have wind speeds of 119 kph (74 mph). They are called 'hurricanes' in the Atlantic and eastern Pacific oceans, 'typhoons' in the North Pacific and the Philippines, and 'cyclones' in the Indian and South Pacific oceans.

▲ Satellite photograph of a hurricane.

Seasonal Occurrences

Hurricanes mostly occur between June and November. Although meteorologists have the basic knowledge of where and when hurricanes can occur, they are unable to predict the exact location of a hurricane before it develops. Hence, a hurricane's path can be forecast only after it has formed.

Christening a Hurricane

All hurricanes are given names that help us identify and track them as they move across the ocean. Short, easy names are chosen to avoid confusion when two or more hurricanes occur at the same time.

▲ A specialist group of pilots, called Hurricane Hunters, fly into the hurricane to gather valuable information that help scientists predict its size, strength and future path.

INTERESTING FACT

The word 'hurricane' is believed to have its origin in the Caribbean islands. This tropical cyclone is believed to have been named after the Carib god of evil and violent storms, Hurican.

FACT FILE

- Clement Wragge, an Australian meteorologist, began giving women's names to tropical storms before the end of the 19th century
- In 1953, the US National Weather Service began using female names for storms
- In 1979, both women's and men's names were used
- One name for each letter of the alphabet is selected, except for Q, U, X, Y and Z

Hurricane Names

The current system of naming hurricanes was adopted in 1979. The World Meteorological Organization chooses hurricane names from lists that are used in rotation. The Atlantic is assigned six lists of names, with one list used each year. Names of huge, destructive hurricanes are 'retired', never to be used again.

▲ A 1949 hurricane was named Bess after the wife of the then US president, Harry Truman.

◄ A pair of square red banners, each with black squares in the middle, are used to warn of hurricanes. These flags are replaced at night by two red lights with a white light placed in-between.

Hurricane Alert

When the weather bureau is certain that a hurricane is about to strike, it puts out a warning in the coastal areas where very strong winds and high waves are expected. The public is informed through television and radio broadcasts, and also by means of flags and lights.

Calm before the Storm

Hurricanes are unpredictable. They can change quickly in size, intensity, speed and direction. Some hurricanes die out, often dumping heavy rain, while others race along at over 95 kph (59 mph). Again, some hurricanes follow a straight path, while others loop around.

The following stages occur before a hurricane

The Eye of the Storm

Hurricanes contain a calm, roughly circular centre called the eye. The eye is an area of clear skies, light winds and no rain. The smaller the eye, the stronger the winds. The eye is the warmest part of the storm. It is surrounded by an 'eyewall' – a dense wall of intense thunderstorms, heavy rains and strong winds. Long bands of rain clouds, called spiral rainbands, spiral into the eyewall.

How a Hurricane is Born

Low air pressure, warm temperatures, moist ocean air and light winds are the right ingredients for a hurricane. When the air above the sea is heated, it rises creating a region of low pressure. The cooler trade winds move into this area. The rotation of the Earth causes the rising air to twist and form a cylinder around an eye. The warm air slowly cools down to produce huge clouds.

How a Hurricane Dies

A hurricane weakens and dies when it travels over land or cold water because its energy source (warm water and heat) is cut off. But it can gather strength once again if it moves to a more favourable location.

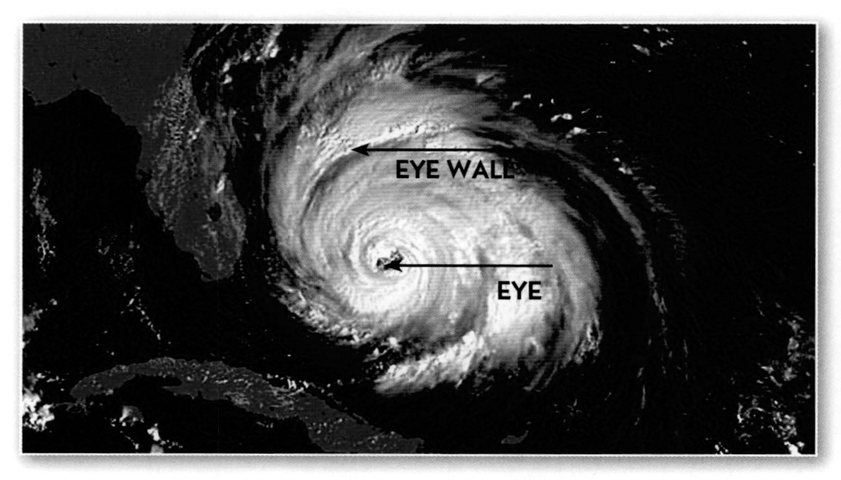

▲ *The warm water vapour in the sea contains energy that is stored in the moist air. When the air rises, this energy is released to form clouds and rain. The release of heat from the vapour warms the air, causing it to rise faster. More moist air is then drawn from the sea, feeding the system with more energy.*

Hurricanes Classified

Hurricanes are classified into five categories based on maximum wind speed. The rating scale is called Saffir-Simpson Hurricane Scale – after Herbert Saffir and Robert Simpson, who developed it.

INTERESTING FACT

Only 3 percent of the heat energy of a hurricane is used up by the fiercely rotating winds. But this energy can equate to six months power supply to the entire United States!

FACT FILE

SAFFIR-SIMPSON HURRICANE SCALE

Category	Wind speed
1 (Weak)	119-153 kph (74-95 mph)
2 (Moderate)	154-177 kph (96-110 mph)
3 (Strong)	178-209 kph (111-130 mph)
4 (Very strong)	210-249 kph (131-155 mph)
5 (Devastating)	249 kph+ (155 mph+)

Hurricane Wary

Hurricanes can cause immense destruction to life and property. Using satellites, scientists can now track hurricanes and issue watches and warnings. A 'watch' cautions that a hurricane is possible within 36 hours, while a 'warning' means that severe weather is already present and there is imminent danger.

Getting Ready for the Storm

You may not be able to leave home for a few days. Hence, a disaster kit containing bottled water, canned food, a radio for news, batteries for flashlights, and medical supplies is a must. Shut off utilities like electricity and gas. Make sure the car has fuel so that you can leave at any time. If there are no evacuation orders, stay indoors. If the wind stops, do not assume the storm is over. It could be the eye of the storm, and the winds will start again.

▸ *Sometimes coastal and low-lying inland areas need to be evacuated due to heavy rains, flash floods and storm surges. In such cases, shelter camps are set up to accommodate those who have lost their homes.*

▾ *Hurricane straps keep roofs attached to walls, while storm shutters protect windows and glass from flying debris and other objects carried by the strong winds.*

Protecting your House

Houses in hurricane-prone areas have special features to protect against high winds and flooding. They are elevated on stilts, so that they are above the high waters that hurricanes bring.

An Emergency Plan for Pets

Disasters like hurricanes and floods affect animals as well. Pets get scared and upset during storms, and they may get injured or stranded. Not all emergency shelters allow animals, so special arrangements need to be made to take care of them.

◂ *Trained teams search for, and rescue, animals that get stranded during natural disasters.*

Listening to the Weather Radio

Weather radios broadcast warnings and watches 24 hours a day. Most weather radios run on batteries. They send out a special alarm tone even when switched off, to alert people about dangerous weather – giving them enough time to take shelter.

Disaster Strikes

Tropical cyclones are the largest and most destructive storms on Earth. At sea, hurricanes spawn powerful winds and tremendous waves. They lead to storm surges – a piling up of water at a storm's centre that can raise the sea level more than 6 metres (20 feet), and even drown a coastline. Heavy rains can cause inland floods and landslides.

Hurricane Andrew, 1992

The costliest US natural disaster was Hurricane Andrew. This deadly storm hit South Florida, causing $26.5 billion in damages.

◀ *Storm surges generated by hurricanes cause immense damage on land.*

Killer Storm Surges

The deadliest natural disaster in US history was the 1900 Galveston, Texas, hurricane, which killed an estimated 8,000 people. Most of the deaths were caused by the storm surge. The 1970 cyclone that hit East Pakistan (present day Bangladesh) caused a storm surge that left about 500,000 people dead.

▲ *Manatees usually locate to sheltered areas near the shore during hurricanes.*

INTERESTING FACT

In Florida, US, manatee deaths caused by boat collisions during 2004 were the lowest in five years. Biologists believe this could be due to the four hurricanes that hit the Florida coast within six weeks – keeping people out of the sea. Only 69 manatees were killed by boats in 2004, as compared to 95 in 2002.

FACT FILE

- **Hurricane David**, 1979: Dominican Republic; winds 277 kph (172 mph); 1,300 dead
- **Hurricane Andrew**, 1992: Florida, Louisiana and the Bahamas; winds 270 kph (168 mph); over 50 dead
- **Hurricane Mitch**, 1998: central America; winds 290 kph (180 mph); about 11,000 dead
- **Hurricane Floyd**, 1999: United States; winds 250 kph (155 mph); some 3 million people evacuated in the largest peacetime exercise of its type in American history

Hurricane Mitch, 1998

Hurricane Mitch was the deadliest Atlantic hurricane since 1780. It raged for 13 days over the Caribbean Sea and the Bahamas. The floods and landslides killed about 11,000 people in Central America, while another 3 million were left homeless.

▼ *Hurricanes - their storm surges, winds and flooding can cause untold damage.*

▲ *Hurricanes cause torrential rains, leading to landslides and floods.*

Hurricane Floyd, 1999

Hurricane Floyd devastated hundreds of miles of the east coast of the United States, from Florida to Maine, causing about $6 billion in flood damage. Most of the 56 deaths were caused by flooding.

A Twisted Story

Tornadoes are violent storms that look like black, funnel-shaped clouds. The wind in these storms can reach speeds of 500 kph (310 mph). Tornadoes are capable of destroying everything in their path.

A Super Tornado

Most severe tornadoes originate in rotating thunderstorms, which form in regions where cold, dry polar winds mix with warm, moist tropical air. These thunderstorms are called supercells, and are characterised by rotating winds, called 'mesocyclones', rising into the storm. The mesocyclone is a spine of wind that spins through the supercells. The wind starts to swirl fast to form a funnel. As the air in the funnel spins faster, it creates a low pressure area that sucks in air and objects.

The most violent tornadoes (F5) can uproot houses and trees.

Tornado Season

Tornadoes can occur at any time of the year. In the southern states of the United States, the peak tornado season is March through May – with May having the most. In the northern states, the peak months are during the summer.

Supercells can come together in a huge cluster and produce a mesocyclone. As the mesocyclone gathers force, it starts to spin faster and extends further towards the ground to form a giant tornado. However, not all mesocyclones form tornadoes.

INTERESTING FACT

Tornadoes can be very strong. There are instances where tornadoes have lifted trees from one place and deposited them hundreds of miles away. A tornado in Minnesota lifted a train almost 25 metres (80 feet) into the air!

FACT FILE

- On an annual average, the United States experiences 100,000 thunderstorms, resulting in over 1,000 tornadoes and about 50 deaths. Most of these are F0 and F1 tornadoes
- F5 tornadoes account for less than 2 percent of all tornadoes in the United States
- On average, 33 tornadoes are reported each year in the United Kingdom

Striking in the Dark

The thunderstorms that produce tornadoes usually take place in the afternoon. Tornadoes are most likely to occur between 3.00 p.m. and 9.00 p.m., but can hit at all hours of the day or night.

Tornado Classification

In 1971, Tetsuya Theodore Fujita created the Fujita Tornado Intensity Scale, which ranks tornadoes by the damage they cause to man made structures. The tornadoes are ranked on an increasing scale from F0 to F5.

Chasing the Storm

Chasing storms is not a profession – it is a hobby, and an expensive one at that! People who chase storms come from all walks of life. Chasers love the challenge and adventure of trying to understand the storm, and taking spectacular photographs and videos!

Important equipment

A well-maintained vehicle is the most important piece of equipment because chasers often cover over 800 kilometres (497 miles) in a day. Chasers also carry cameras and camcorders, radios, scanners, miniature TVs, micro-cassette recorders, first-aid kits and road atlases. They may also have laptops, GPS tracking, anemometers and thermometers.

▼ *Storm chasers use a variety of vehicles – from sedans and vans to pickup trucks. However, sports utility vehicles (SUVs) are the most useful.*

Dangers on the road

Storm chasers must be alert to every situation and have a backup plan at hand. Strong winds can overturn a chase vehicle or blow out windows. Hail can damage vehicles and equipment, and be a traffic hazard. Flash flooding can leave chasers suddenly stranded. Driving in rough weather is dangerous and can cause crashes.

◄ *The Doppler radar unit can spot a mesocyclone two to four hours before it forms into a tornado, thereby vastly aiding in predicting tornadoes.*

INTERESTING FACT

Storm spotting is carried out by unpaid volunteers who serve their local communities. A spotter's main function is to report critical weather information to the weather office. Being a spotter is not the same thing as being a chaser, although many people choose to do both.

FACT FILE

- An estimated 1,000 storm chasers travel beyond their hometown area during any given season
- On average, chasers see a tornado once every five or ten trips
- Roger Jensen was the first person who actively hunted for tornadoes, in the upper Midwest, US, in the late 1940s

Most 'Chaseable' Tornadoes

The most 'chaseable' tornadoes are those that occur during daylight and travel in open country. Also, they should not be moving too fast, and nor should they be so wrapped in clouds and rain that they are difficult to see. These types of tornadoes are the most common in Tornado Alley.

Tornado Alley

Compared with other kinds of storms, tornadoes are rare, which is probably the reason why scientists still do not fully understand how tornadoes form, grow and die. Tornadoes can last from a few seconds to more than an hour. They might remain on the ground for just a few yards, or travel across more than 160 kilometres (100 miles).

Waterspout

A waterspout is a tornado that passes over water. It is a funnel-shaped storm consisting of wind, water and ocean spray. It is generally weaker than a land based tornado. Waterspouts occur most frequently in warm tropical waters.

▲ *Sometimes, waterspouts can move over land and cause considerable damage. In fact, many of the tornadoes along the Gulf Coast originate in the Gulf of Mexico as waterspouts.*

Tornado Alley

Some regions of the world have a higher frequency of tornadoes than others. One such place is known as Tornado Alley in the United States, and refers to the region on the Great Plains extending from central Texas to the Canadian border. The conditions there favour the formation of the most severe tornadoes in spring and early summer, earning it the name Tornado Alley.

▲ *Tornadoes are most frequent in Tornado Alley during April- June, with the highest occurrence in Oklahoma, Texas and Florida.*

Over the Hills

Hills and mountains do not shelter against tornadoes – the twisters can go over them. The F4 tornado that hit the Teton Wilderness near Jackson in Wyoming, US, on July 21, 1987, went over mountains as high as 3,000 metres (9,843 feet), knocking down pine trees 24-30 metres (80-100 feet) tall!

Storm from the Gulf of Mexico

In late winter and early spring, tornadoes occur quite often in the states bordering the Gulf of Mexico. These tornadoes are formed when warm moist air from the Gulf of Mexico to the south and cold Arctic air just to the north collides over the midwest and southern United States.

INTERESTING FACT

The word 'tornado' has been derived from the Spanish 'tornear', meaning to turn, or twist. Tornadoes are formed by rotating winds, and hence are given the name. Tornadoes are also called 'twisters' for the same reason.

FACT FILE

- Tornadoes have hit all 50 states in the United States, though this does not happen every year
- Tornadoes are most common in the spring and early summer
- Kansas has had the highest number of F5 tornadoes since 1880
- Iowa has the greatest number of F5 tornadoes per square mile
- Kentucky has the highest percentage of all tornadoes ranked as violent (F4 or F5)

Safety and Rescue

The biggest danger during a tornado is from flying debris. Debris accounts for a large part of the damage and many of the injuries and deaths. Although tornadoes are rare, people who live in areas where an occurrence is possible should know what to do to protect themselves.

Facing the Storm

When conditions are right, meteorologists issue tornado watches and warnings. People also rely on weather radios, which sound an alarm even when turned off. A tornado watch sounds an alert for approaching storms. A warning means a tornado has been spotted, and people should be ready to take shelter immediately.

▸ *An ideal tornado shelter should include blankets, bottled water, radios and first-aid kits.*

SAFETY AND PREPAREDNESS

- Stay calm and alert
- Seek shelter in a basement, a small closet, or a bathroom
- Stay away from windows. Broken glass can cause injuries
- Protect your body with a mattress or blankets
- Evacuate mobile homes and find shelter in a solid structure
- If you are caught on a highway, do not seek shelter under an overpass
- Do not seek shelter in a vehicle
- Do not try to outrun a tornado in your car
- Listen for reports on a portable radio
- Keep a weather radio with batteries if you live in an area with a lot of tornadoes

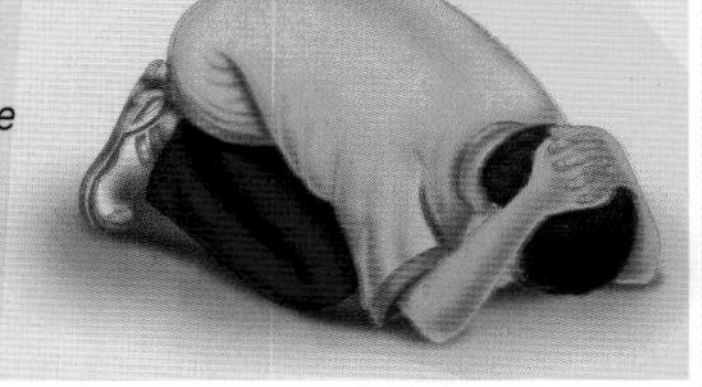

▸ *If you are out in the open, find a ditch or depression and lie low.*

Storm Shelter

Storm shelters are small structures made of concrete, steel, or reinforced fibreglass. They can be both above the ground or underground. Shelters must meet the set standards for construction, size and strength. They must be strong enough to protect against wind-borne debris and withstand tremendous wind pressures.

▴ *Scientists are experimenting with unique ways to control tornadoes. One of these is called cloud seeding. Here, dry ice is fed into the mesocyclone to prevent tornado formation. The idea is to force heavy rainfall and thus weaken the storm. However, the experiment is currently in the initial stages.*

▸ *Search teams use dogs to assist in locating victims, saving on both time and manpower.*

Spinning out of Control

Today we know what tornadoes are, and that they can kill hundreds and cause immense damage. Until the mid-1900s, however, people were not aware of this destructive force. In fact, tornado forecasting and record-keeping began only in 1950. Hence, we do not have accurate information about tornadoes before that date.

The Biggest Outbreak

The Super Outbreak of April 3-4, 1974, was the worst tornado outbreak in US history, with 148 twisters striking 13 states. The impact was felt in Canada as well. It lasted 16 hours, killing 330 people and injuring 5,484, in a damage path covering about 4,000 kilometres (2,485 miles). Seven tornadoes were rated F5 and 23 more were rated F4.

▼ *On November 10, 2002, several tornadoes swept through the small town of Mossy Grove in Tennessee, US, killing eight people.*

Tri-State Tornado, 1925

The Tri-State Tornado Outbreak of March 18, 1925, killed 695 people as it raced along at 96-117 kph (60-73 mph) across the US states of Missouri, Illinois and Indiana. The F5 category storm produced the most known tornado fatalities in a single city or town: at least 234 died at Murphysboro, Illinois. It remains uncertain whether it was one tornado or a 'family' of tornadoes that caused the damage.

▶ *The state of Missouri, US, has experienced some of the deadliest tornadoes.*

Palm Sunday, April 11, 1965

The Palm Sunday Outbreak in the United States produced 51 tornadoes within a span of 12 hours. Indiana, Ohio and Michigan were the hardest hit. The tornadoes killed 256 people and caused more than $200 million in damages.

▲ *Aerial pictures of destruction in Kansas City, US, during the May 2003 tornado*

Killer Tornadoes

The United States witnessed one of its deadliest tornado outbreaks on May 4, 2003. About 84 tornadoes are said to have struck eight states, making it one of the top 10 outbreaks ever. At least 38 people were killed in Kansas, Missouri and Tennessee. The tornado onslaught continued as the twisters touched down in Oklahoma.

INTERESTING FACT

A Doppler radar mounted on a truck measured a tornado wind speed of 512 kph (318 mph) in Moore, Oklahoma, on May 3, 1999. This was the strongest wind ever recorded near the Earth's surface. It is extremely rare to get a direct measurement of a tornado wind speed like this one, since ordinary weather instruments are blown away or broken long before winds reach these kinds of speeds. Because of this, nobody knows the highest wind speed in a tornado.

FACT FILE

- Single month with the most tornadoes: In the United States, the record for the most tornadoes in a month was set in May 2003 – with 516 tornadoes confirmed. This broke the old mark of 399, set in June 1992
- Biggest known tornado: The F4 tornado that hit the town of Hallam in Nebraska, US, on May 22, 2004, set a record for peak width at nearly two and half miles

▼ *The 1896 tornado that hit St. Louis, Missouri, left over 250 dead.*

Hurricanes vs Tornadoes

Hurricanes and tornadoes are both powerful storms, but with several differences. Hurricanes, due to their size, are easily spotted and can be tracked for days before they strike. Tornadoes form quickly, with only a few minutes' warning, and travel in unpredictable directions.

A hurricane's path or direction varies, but tornadoes tend to travel from the southwest to a north-east direction.

The air circulating around the eyes of both hurricanes and tornadoes, moves in a counter-clockwise direction; but the eye of a hurricane is very much larger (up to 80 km, or 50 miles, across) than the eye of a tornado (only a few feet in diameter).

Causes

Hurricanes are formed over warm ocean water. On the other hand, tornadoes develop over land as the result of dry air colliding with warm humid air.

Appearance

Hurricanes consist of thunderstorms wrapped in spiral bands around the storm's centre. A tornado hangs from the bottom of a single thunderstorm as a funnel-shaped cloud that touches the ground.

Duration

The average hurricane lasts for a week, varying anywhere from two to ten days. Most tornadoes last for only a few minutes or perhaps half an hour, although a few have lasted up to seven hours.

Hurricanes cause more overall destruction than tornadoes because of their much larger size, longer duration, and other side effects like storm surge and flash flooding.

Damage

Hurricanes cause widespread damage, and are measured on the Saffir-Simpson scale, from C1 to C5. Tornadoes cause localised damage, and are rated on the Fujita scale, from F0 to F5.

INTERESTING FACT

El Niño and La Niña are phenomena associated with major changes in the sea-surface temperatures in the tropical Pacific. Meteorologists agree that El Niño influences large-scale weather patterns, but so far they have not found that either El Niño or La Niña directly causes tornadoes.

FACT FILE

- A hurricane is over 480-800 km (298-497 miles) in diameter, while a large tornado could be just a mile across
- The wind speed of a hurricane is 119-257 kph (74-160 mph), while that of a tornado is 322- 483 kph (200-300 mph)
- Weather forecasters can predict a hurricane for a wide area about two or three days ahead, and can more precisely predict the location of a hurricane 6-10 hours beforehand. Tornado warnings are issued 20 minutes or less before the storm hits

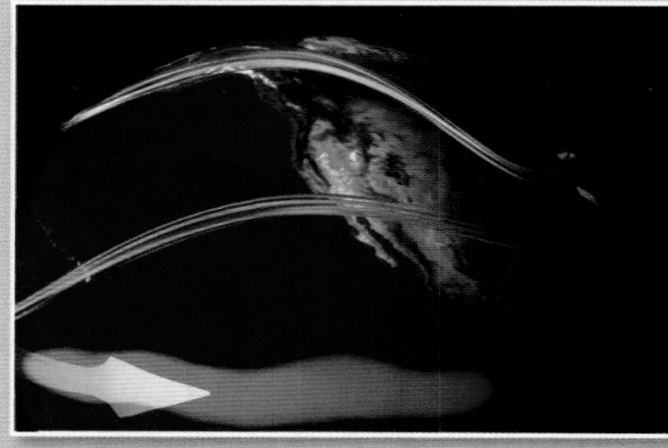

El Niño brings about unusually warm ocean conditions in the tropical Pacific, near the Equator

Stormy Side Effects

Both hurricanes and tornadoes are accompanied by heavy rains, hailstorms and powerful winds. However, compared to tornadoes, hurricanes cause much more overall damage individually over a season and over much larger areas.

Dangers and Hazards

Hurricanes can damage structures through storm surge and flooding, as well as with their strong winds. Coastal flooding is probable along low-lying areas. In comparison, tornadoes are less destructive. However, the spinning winds of powerful tornadoes can suck people and animals in, uproot trees and houses and carry off vehicles.

In the Storm's Wake

Storms can leave behind long-term effects that are devastating, especially in the case of hurricanes. Once the storm has passed, people in the affected area face the danger of disease epidemics and starvation. Damage to bridges, roads and railroads hinder rescue missions. Damaged telephone lines and electricity poles result in a breakdown of communication and cause power outages.

Storm Surge

A storm surge is a rise in the ocean level caused by strong winds from a hurricane. The ocean waters sweep along the coastline near where the eye of the storm crosses the land, and can cause dangerous flooding – even in areas many miles inland.

Danger at Sea

Hurricanes are also a threat to sailors out at sea. Ships and boats can be tossed around, hurled against cliffs, or engulfed by waves. A small craft advisory is issued when wind speeds are between 20 and 33 knots.

▶ *Heavy rains caused by hurricanes can lead to landslides, sweeping away houses and people.*

Forecasting at First

Scientists have been studying tornadoes and hurricanes for about a hundred years. Today, with computer modelling and satellite imagery, meteorologists can track and forecast these great storms with increasing accuracy.

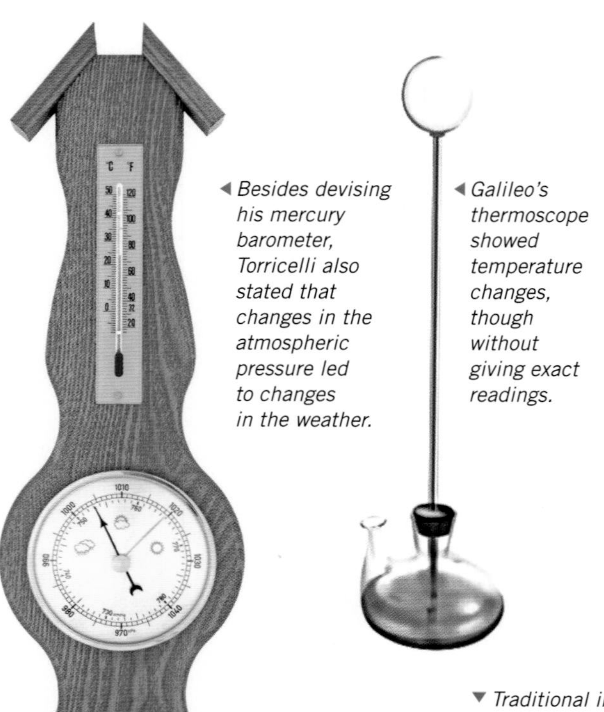

Besides devising his mercury barometer, Torricelli also stated that changes in the atmospheric pressure led to changes in the weather.

Galileo's thermoscope showed temperature changes, though without giving exact readings.

Early Weather Instruments

In ancient times, weather forecasts were made by merely observing the skies – clear skies for fair weather and black clouds for a storm! Finally, in the early 1600s, Italian scientist Galileo Galilei invented the thermoscope, an instrument that could detect temperature changes. In 1643, Galileo's pupil, Evangelista Torricelli, invented the barometer to measure the pressure of air in the atmosphere. Later, the hygrometer and the mercury thermometer helped make weather forecasting a reality.

Early Forecasts

In the late 1700s, French scientist Laurent Lavoisier said that weather could be predicted a couple of days ahead by using daily readings of atmospheric pressure, humidity, temperature, wind speed and direction. By the 20th century, equipment like the radiosonde were developed. It consists of a small box containing a thermometer, a hygrometer and a barometer. It is attached to a balloon that bursts upon reaching a certain height. The instrument collects information on temperature, pressure, humidity, and wind speed and direction.

Traditional instruments like the thermometer and barometer are still used to predict weather conditions like hurricanes and tornadoes.

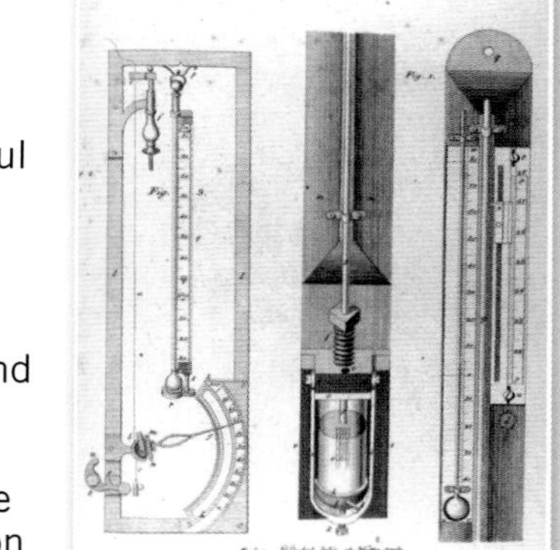

To Predict a Hurricane

It was in 1875 that the first successful hurricane forecast was made. Benito Viñes, a Spanish priest and director of the Meteorological Observatory in Havana, Cuba, had made detailed observations about previous storms and studied the wind and cloud patterns of hurricanes. On September 11, 1875, he published his first hurricane forecast in a newspaper. His prediction helped to save several lives when the storm hit the Cuban coast two days later! Today, meteorologists use various instruments to make hurricane warnings.

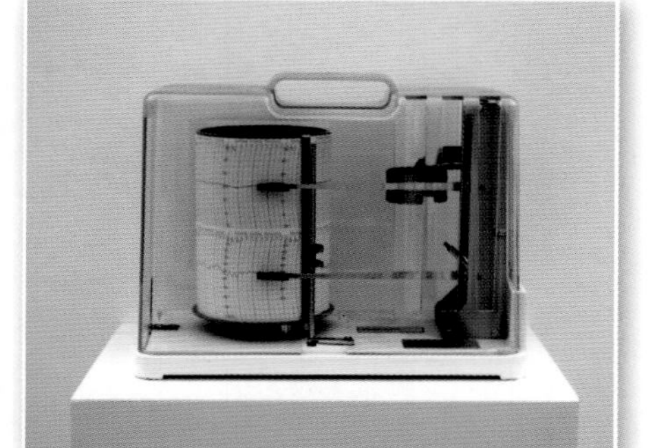

The hygrometer measures the water vapour quantity in air, thus indicating humidity levels.

INTERESTING FACT

During the 1970s, scientists began mobile storm research programmes. One of these was the Totable Tornado Observatory (TOTO). It was placed in the path of a tornado to verify wind speed, direction, temperature and atmospheric pressure. However, the TOTO was often destroyed by high-speed winds, and was replaced by Doppler radars.

FACT FILE

- 1494 Christopher Columbus shelters his fleet from a tropical cyclone, and writes the first European account of a hurricane
- 1743 Ben Franklin suggests that hurricanes do not move in the same direction as the winds
- 1831 William Redfield finds that hurricane winds swirl in a counter-clockwise pattern. He begins compiling hurricane tracks
- 1875 Benito Viñes issues his first hurricane warning.

Forecasting and Observation

Once hurricanes and tornadoes form, scientists track their location using various tools and instruments, but it is difficult to predict the exact path of a storm because its direction, speed and intensity can quickly change. Forecasters can only issue warnings to people in the storm's probable path.

▲ *Weather balloons, filled with helium gas, record conditions in the upper layers of the atmosphere.*

Monitoring Hurricanes

When hurricanes are still far out in the ocean, they are monitored mainly by satellites, and also by ships and buoys. When within 322 kilometres (200 miles) of the coast, radar provides measurements of the storm. Computer models are used to forecast storm intensity and movement.

Artificial satellites are launched into space by multistage carrier rockets.

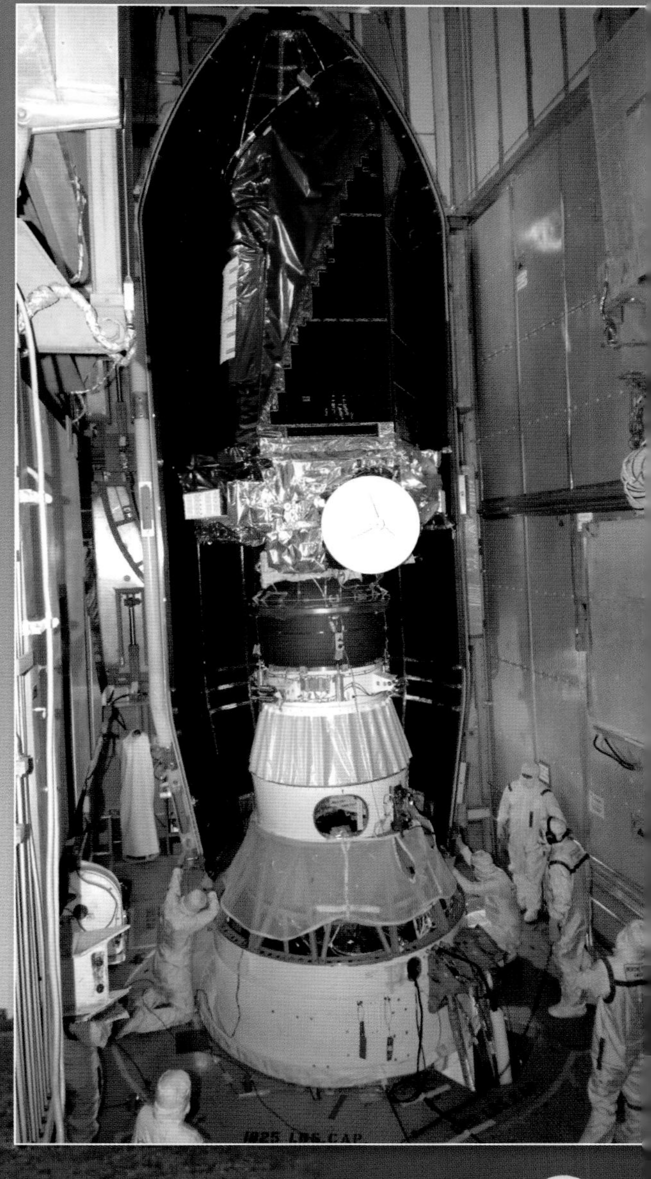

Eye in the Sky

Radar and weather satellites are the main tools used to forecast severe weather. The Doppler weather radar can detect strong rotation within storms, and thus help forecasters make timely and specific warnings of approaching tornadoes.

When Every Minute Counts

With advances in technology, scientists can now issue warnings before tornadoes even form. The average lead time for warnings has increased from 5-6 minutes in the early 1990s, to 10-11 minutes today.

INTERESTING FACT

The GPS dropwindsonde is a modified version of the radiosonde. It is dropped by an aircraft flying into a hurricane. The instrument uses a parachute to descend slowly through the hurricane. The dropwindsonde collects information and radios it back to the aircraft.

FACT FILE

- Forecasters track a hurricane's movement using latitude and longitude - used to pinpoint any position on the globe
- A Doppler radar measures how fast rain or hail is moving towards or away from the radar. The farther away from the radar a storm is, the less accurate the measurements.
- In the 1980s, Doppler radars were used in warning operations as the NEXRAD (NEXt generation weather RADar) programme. NEXRAD is a computer Doppler system designed to track and analyse tornado-producing storms
- In the United States, only the National Weather Service (NWS) issues tornado forecasts nationwide

◄ *Geostationary weather satellites orbit over the Equator, while polar-orbiting satellites pass over the polar regions.*

Super Survivors

Imagine being caught in the middle of a severe tornado or hurricane, and living to tell the tale! Here are a few remarkable true stories of some very lucky people who survived tornadoes, lightning strikes, hurricanes and storm surges.

Surviving a Tornado

On December 17, 2000, an F4 tornado ripped through Tuscaloosa county in Alabama, US, killing 12 people and destroying over a hundred homes. But John Bibby and his wife managed to survive. About 10 years earlier, Bibby had built a makeshift underground shelter outside his house. When the warning sirens sounded on the fateful day, the couple, along with their two dogs, took refuge in the shelter.

▲ David Ledford of Asheville, North Carolina, US, and his dog, Angel, survived the wrath of Hurricane.

Surviving a storm surge

Mary Ann of Mississippi survived the storm surge caused by Hurricane Camille in 1969. As the building began to collapse, Mary floated out of the window and grabbed on to anything she could find – pieces of furniture and tree branches. About 12 hours later, she was found some 6 kilometres (4 miles) from her apartment. Although severely injured, Mary soon recovered.

◀ John Bibby climbing out of his shelter.

Surviving a Lightning Bolt

Gene Moore and his friends were struck by lightning while storm-chasing in Oklahoma on May 23, 1981. Luckily all of them survived. The men did not realise that they were in danger because they saw no lightning, thunder or rain, even though a tornado had touched down a mile and half way!

▲ *The tornado that struck Cordell, Oklahoma, on October 9, 2001, wreaked havoc by destroying several buildings. This local motel was one of the victims of the storm. Miraculously, though, an elderly couple survived the onslaught by standing beneath the doorframe shown in the photograph.*

Surviving Hurricane Andrew

The Benitez family of Homestead, Florida, survived Hurricane Andrew in 1992 by taking shelter in a small closet. And for two days they remained standing there because it was flooded. They did not have anything to eat all that time, since the strong winds had blown away everything. Only three walls and the roof of their house remained by the end of the storm.

▼ *In 1999, when Hurricane Dennis struck the coasts of North Carolina, houses in Kitty Hawk remained undamaged due to their elevation.*

INTERESTING FACT

Houses in hurricane areas are built in a special way to survive storms. They are raised on long stilts, looking like long-legged birds, so they are above the high water and floods that a hurricane brings. Special straps hold down the roofs during high winds. Storm shutters protect windows.

FACT FILE

- The F5 tornado that hit Xenia, Ohio, in April 1974 smashed Victor Gregory's farmhouse, but left three fragile things intact: a mirror, a case of eggs, and a box of Christmas ornaments
- A tornado picked up a baby girl from a buggy at Uren in Saskatchewan, Canada, in 1923. Hours later, she was found asleep in a shack two miles away
- In a famous incident, farmer Will Keller of Kansas was sucked into the funnel of a tornado in 1928, and survived it
- On July 1, 1955, nine-year-old Sharon Weron and her horse were carried by a South Dakota tornado over a hill and across a valley, and dropped about 305 metres (1,000 feet) away

In Legend and Fiction

The destructive power of storms like hurricanes and tornadoes inspires both fear and fascination. It's no surprise that humans throughout time have tried to control these storms. Ancient tribes were known to make offerings to the 'weather gods' to appease them.

Weather Gods Around the World

People in ancient times believed that violent storms were brought on by angry weather gods. In Yoruba mythology, Oya, the female warrior, is the goddess of fire, wind and thunder. When she is angry, she creates tornadoes and hurricanes. In Egyptian legend, Set is regarded as the god of storms.

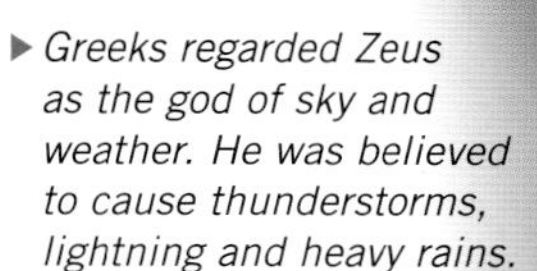

▶ *Greeks regarded Zeus as the god of sky and weather. He was believed to cause thunderstorms, lightning and heavy rains.*

◀ *In ancient Egypt, the god Set was associated with natural disasters like hurricanes, thunderstorms, lightning, earthquakes and eclipses.*

Hurricanes in Mayan Mythology

The Mayan people believed that when Hurakan, the god of lightning, blew his breath across the water, he brought forth dry land. Every year the Mayans threw a young woman into the sea as a sacrifice to please Hurakan. A warrior was also sacrificed to lead the girl to Hurakan's underwater kingdom.

The Bear Brings Winter Hurricanes

In Iroquois mythology, Ga-oh is the wind giant, whose house is guarded by several animals, each representing a specific type of wind. The Bear is the north wind who brings winter hurricanes, and he can crush the world with his storms or destroy it with cold.

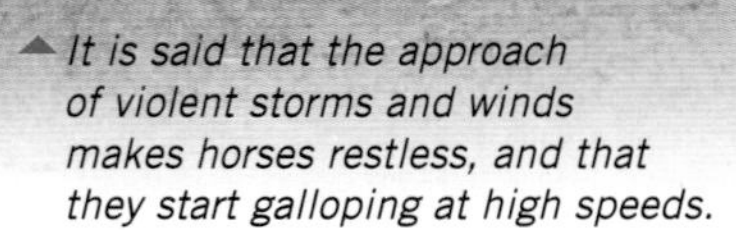

It is said that the approach of violent storms and winds makes horses restless, and that they start galloping at high speeds.

Tornado Oddities

For a long time, people believed that tornadoes were capable of all sorts of things: sucking the water from wells; making buildings explode; or even pulling the feathers off chickens. But these 'oddities' were either lies or just misunderstandings of the actual events. Another popular but misplaced belief was that tornadoes were deflected by rivers and hills.

INTERESTING FACT

In Babylonian mythology, Marduk, the god of gods, defeated the bad tempered goddess Tiamat with the help of a hurricane. When the other gods learned about Tiamat's plans to destroy them, they turned to Marduk for help. Armed with bows and arrows, winds and a hurricane, Marduk captured Tiamat and let the hurricane fill her jaws and stomach. Then he shot an arrow into her belly and killed her.

FACT FILE

- It was thought that a hill called Burnett's Mound protected Topeka, Kansas. However, on June 8, 1966, a violent tornado went directly over Burnett's Mound on its way into Topeka
- The first sound recording of a tornado's roar (like the sound of a freight train) was made during the 1974 Xenia tornado. Thomas Yougen turned his tape recorder on as the tornado approached the city

In Aztec mythology, the serpent god Quetzalcoatl was also the god of the winds. He was also believed to have been the Sun.

Marduk became lord of all the gods after killing the dragon goddess.

nside the Earth

The ground under your feet may feel strong and firm, but the inside of the Earth is not. The topmost covering of the Earth is called the crust. The crust has three layers under it: the mantle, the outer core and the inner core. The crust and the upper mantle make up the lithosphere.

Atmosphere
Outer core
Inner core
Mantle
Crust

▲ *Although the inner core is 5,000-6,000°C, the extremely high pressures make the core seem solid.*

Hot as the Sun

The mantle is a thick layer of rock below the crust and is made up of oxides of silicon, aluminium, iron and magnesium. Next comes the outer core, which is in molten liquid form. At the centre of the Earth is the inner core and it is believed to be as hot as the Sun!

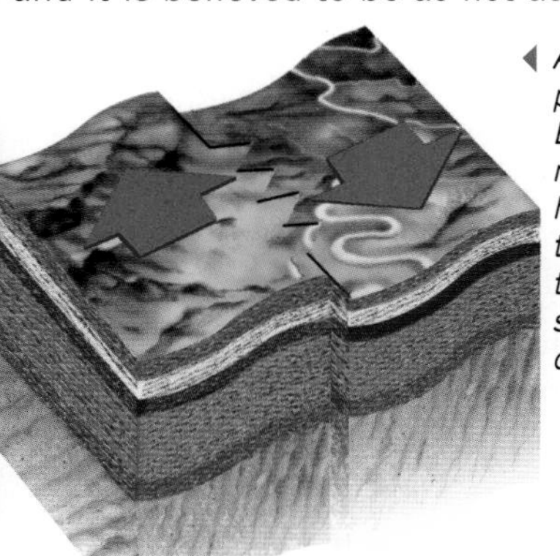

◀ *As the tectonic plates on the Earth's crust move, they often hit each other at the edge. Here the plates are sliding past each other.*

◀ *Volcanic eruptions throw up three types of material: lava, rocks and gases.*

◀ *When tectonic plates strike against each other, one plate usually slides over the other.*

Throwing up Fire

When the Earth spews out molten rock from deep within, it does it via volcanoes. Volcanoes are openings on the Earth's surface through which lava, hot gases and rock fragments erupt.

Like a Football

Just as a football has many joints on its surface, the Earth's crust is also made of rocky plates placed next to each other. These are called tectonic plates. But unlike a football, these plates are not joined and often collide with each other.

Getting Shaky

Most earthquakes occur along the boundaries of these rocky plates. These plates slip against each other, causing the Earth to jolt suddenly – either gently or really violently!

INTERESTING FACT

The upper part of the mantle has a temperature of about 870°C. This temperature gradually increases down through the mantle to about 2200°C near the outer core. In the core, the temperature may be as high as 7000°C.

FACT FILE

DEPTH FROM EARTH'S SURFACE

- Mantle: Up to 2,900 km (1,802 miles)
- Outer core: Up to 5,150 km (3,200 miles)
- Inner core: Up to 6,400 km (3,977 miles)

Volcanoes

An erupting volcano is perhaps one of the most spectacular sights on Earth. Volcanoes are like nature's own fireworks – but these are much more powerful and dangerous. A violent eruption can blow apart an entire mountain.

Awesome Power

Powerful forces within the Earth cause volcanoes. An opening on the Earth's surface is formed, through which lava, hot gases and rock fragments spew out.

Melting Magma

Extreme heat inside the Earth melts the rocks to form magma and gas. The gas-filled magma slowly rises toward the Earth's surface from the mantle. As more magma rises, it forms a large chamber near the surface.

Venting Out

From the chamber the magma melts a channel, or conduit, to rise up to the surface. Conduits are formed in weaker areas of the Earth's surface. As the magma approaches the surface, it blasts out through an opening called the central vent.

Spitting Fire

With some eruptions, huge fiery clouds rise over the mountain, and glowing streams of lava flow down its sides. In others, red-hot ash and cinders shoot out of the mountaintop, and large lumps of hot rock are thrown out high into the air.

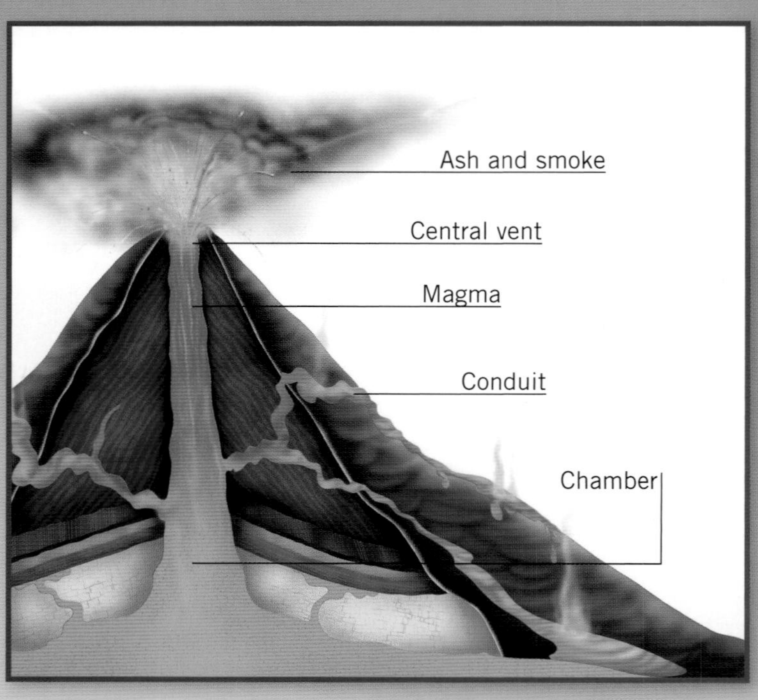

▲ *The volcanic materials gradually build up around the vent, forming a volcanic mountain, or volcano.*

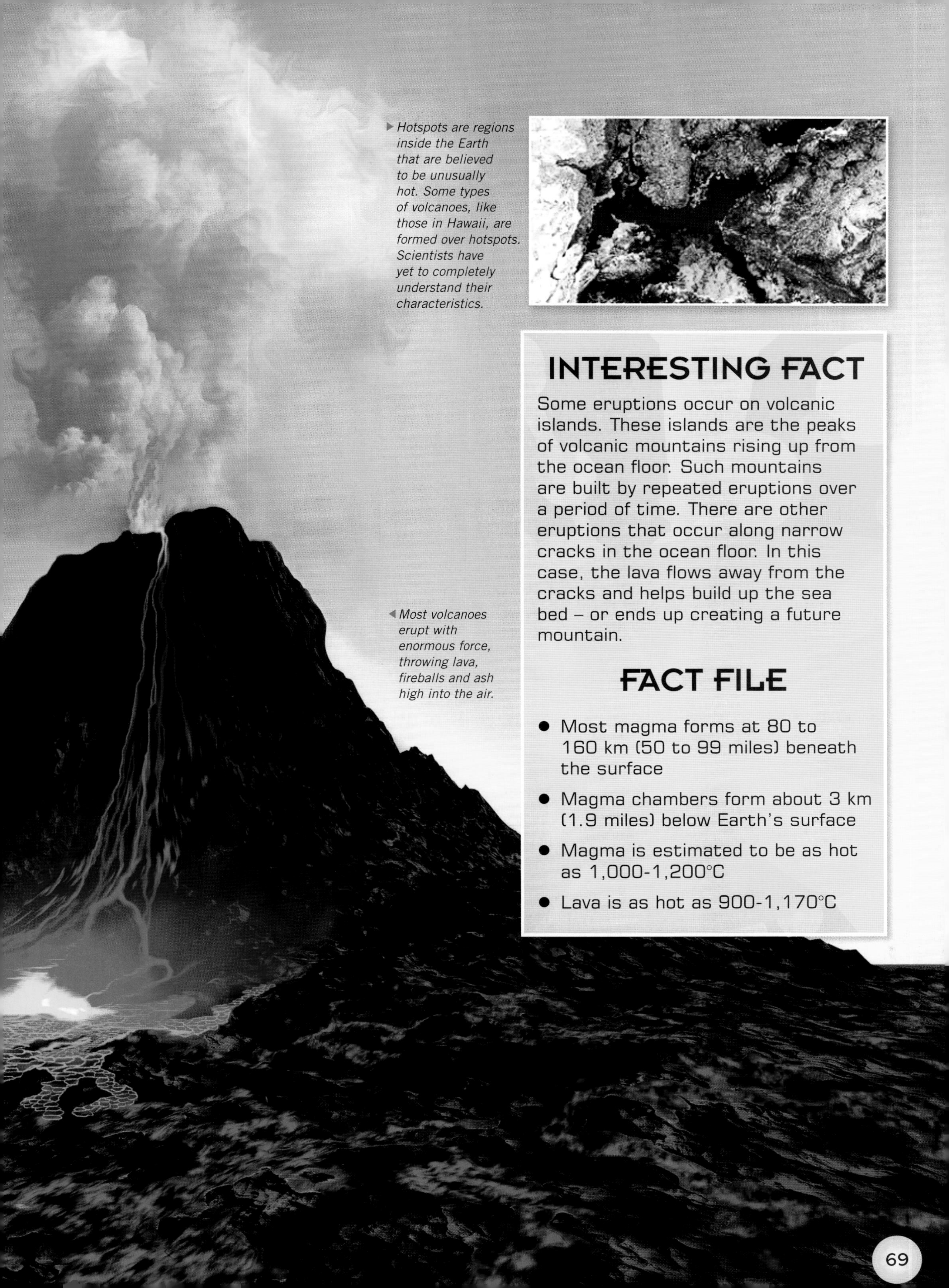

▶ *Hotspots are regions inside the Earth that are believed to be unusually hot. Some types of volcanoes, like those in Hawaii, are formed over hotspots. Scientists have yet to completely understand their characteristics.*

◀ *Most volcanoes erupt with enormous force, throwing lava, fireballs and ash high into the air.*

INTERESTING FACT

Some eruptions occur on volcanic islands. These islands are the peaks of volcanic mountains rising up from the ocean floor. Such mountains are built by repeated eruptions over a period of time. There are other eruptions that occur along narrow cracks in the ocean floor. In this case, the lava flows away from the cracks and helps build up the sea bed – or ends up creating a future mountain.

FACT FILE

- Most magma forms at 80 to 160 km (50 to 99 miles) beneath the surface
- Magma chambers form about 3 km (1.9 miles) below Earth's surface
- Magma is estimated to be as hot as 1,000-1,200°C
- Lava is as hot as 900-1,170°C

Volcano Classification

Not all volcanoes are alike and scientists define them in many ways – depending on how often they erupt, their shape, the kind of molten rock they are made of, and more.

▲Lava eruption at Kilauea Iki, a crater situated east of the active Kilauea volcano in the Hawaii Island.

On and Off

Active volcanoes are those that either erupt constantly or have erupted recently. Although generally quiet, they can be violent at times. Intermittent volcanoes erupt at regular periods, while dormant volcanoes are generally quiet and they have become inactive for a while, but an eruption is possible again. Extinct volcanoes have been inactive during recorded history. They probably will never erupt again.

Free-Flowing

Shield volcanoes are formed when a large amount of free-flowing lava spills from a vent and spreads widely. The lava slowly builds up a low, broad and dome-shaped mountain. Thousands of separate, overlapping lava streams (each less than 15 metres (49 feet) thick) formed Mauna Loa in Hawaii.

Layered On

Composite volcanoes are formed when both lava and rock fragments erupt from a central vent. These materials pile up in alternate layers around the vent. Several such layers build up into a towering (and usually cone-shaped) mountain.

▲Mt Kilimanjaro is a dormant, snow-capped volcano. Located in Tanzania, it is the highest mountain in Africa.

Conically Inclined

Cinder cones build up when mostly rocky material erupts and falls back to gather around the vent. The accumulated material – mostly cinders – forms a cone-shaped mountain with a bowl-shaped crater at the top. Their height can vary from a few metres to several hundreds of metres.

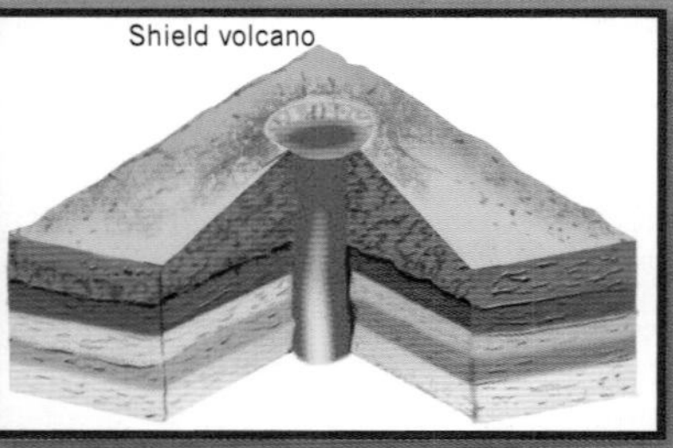

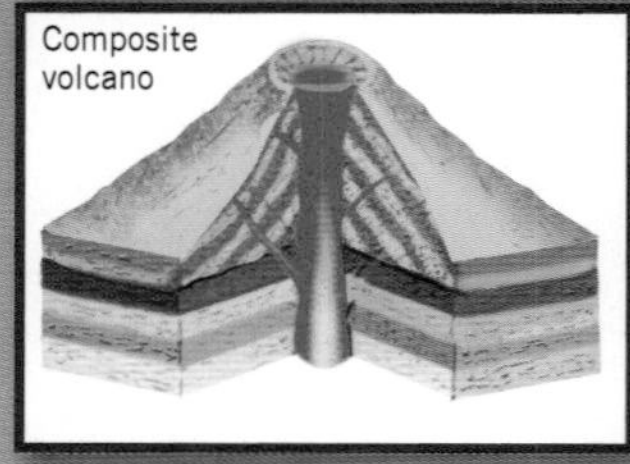

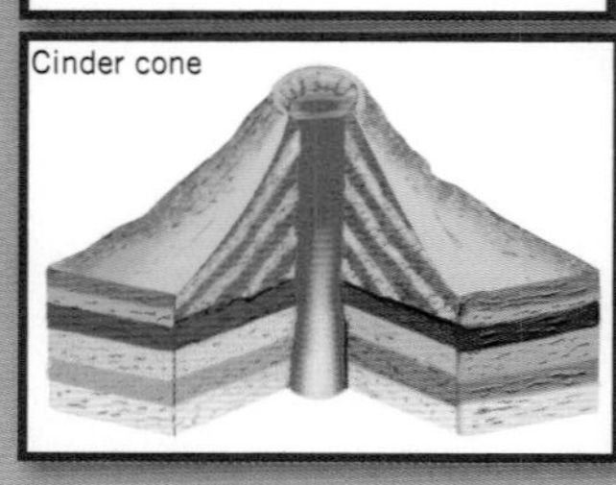

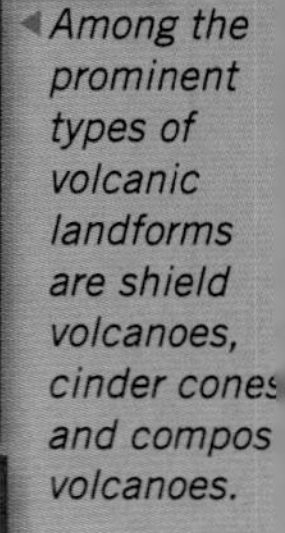

◄Among the prominent types of volcanic landforms are shield volcanoes, cinder cones and compos volcanoes.

▼Lassen Volcanic National Park at the Cascade Range in northern California, US, features the Lassen volcanic peak. The volcano erupted last in 1921.

Volcanoes Under Sea

Most volcanic eruptions occur on the ocean floor. These submarine eruptions occur along narrow cracks in the ocean floor and the lava flows away from the cracks, building up the sea bed or the sea crust. However, nobody has yet observed a deep submarine eruption live.

Pillow lava is formed when molten rock comes in contact with cold seawater or when eruptions occur in the sea.

Invisible

Since most submarine eruptions occur in the deep, they cannot be seen from the surface. Only special features formed by the volcanic action have been observed. Submarine volcanoes can lead to island formation, as the erupted lava and volcanic matter accumulate over many years.

Cool and Solid

The high pressure exerted by the water makes oceanic volcanoes behave differently from the ones situated on land. The pressure keeps the gases and steam in solution, preventing any violent explosion. So in this case, the lava flows down the slopes quietly in blocks, spreading out in a pillow-like manner. The lava cools down quickly to become solid, and tends to collect along the sides of the slope.

The mid-ocean ridge system encircles the Earth like the seams of a baseball. The Earth's crust on these seams is continually moving apart, creating new ocean floor. The ridges have thousands of individual volcanoes that erupt periodically.

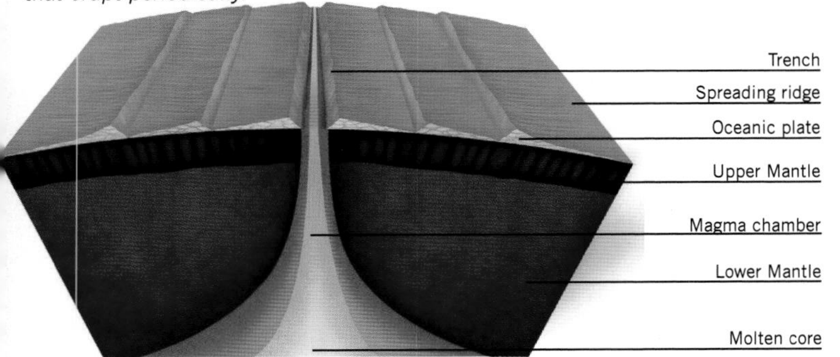

Sand and Rubble

Lava erupting from volcanoes on a shallow sea floor, or flowing into the sea from land, cools very rapidly. This splits the lava into sand and rubble, which may get deposited in coastal areas, as in the case of the famous 'black sand' beaches of Hawaii.

The black sand beaches of Hawaii were created by the violent interaction between hot lava and seawater.

Shallow Waters

When volcanoes erupt in shallow waters, they can blast steam and rock debris high above the sea surface. The ocean currents can cause the debris to drift over a large area, although most debris is deposited on the sea floor.

INTERESTING FACT

Although toxic to most living organisms, some exotic and specially adapted life forms live near the vents of submarine volcanoes. The lava creates the edges of new oceanic plates and also helps in producing heat and chemicals that support certain living organisms.

FACT FILE

- **Numbers**: Estimated at over a million worldwide
- **Average depth**: About 2,600 metres (8,500 feet)
- **Mid-ocean ridges produce**: About 75 percent of the magma worldwide

Rocks and Minerals

Three main kinds of materials can erupt from a volcano. These are lava, rock fragments and gas. The material that comes out of volcanoes depends chiefly on how sticky or fluid the magma is.

Red-Hot

Lava is the name for magma that has escaped to the Earth's surface. When lava reaches the surface, it is extremely hot. Then, as it starts to cool down, the lava hardens into different kinds of rock matter.

▲ *The ocean floor is mostly made up of basalt, which is formed by lava flowing from cracks in the mid-ocean ridge.*

Rocky Matter

Igneous rocks such as basalt are formed as lava cools above the ground. Such rocks are also created when the magma gets trapped in small pockets inside the Earth. These cool off slowly to form igneous rocks like granite.

Mineral Mine

Most of the metallic minerals mined in the world – such as copper, gold, silver, lead and zinc – are a result of volcanic activities over the years. These minerals are found in magma deep in the roots of extinct volcanoes, and are mined from there.

Blasting Tephra

Rock fragments called tephra originate in 'sticky' magma. Since the magma is sticky, it does not allow any gas to escape. The trapped gas builds up so much pressure that it blasts the magma into fragments. Tephra includes volcanic dust, volcanic ash and volcanic bombs.

INTERESTING FACT

Volcanic dust can be carried vast distances. In 1883, the eruption of Krakatoa in Indonesia sent dust some 27 kilometres (17 miles) up into the air. The dust flew around the Earth several times and produced luminous red sunsets in many parts of the world.

FACT FILE

- Lava temperature: More than 1,100°C
- Volcanic dust: Diameter less than 0.25 millimetre
- Volcanic ash: Diameter less than 0.5 centimetre
- Volcanic bomb: Diameter over 64 millimetres (2.5 inches)

◀ *The violet-coloured amethyst is a form of the mineral quartz and is prized as a gem stone.*

▼ *Diamonds are brought to the surface from the mantle in an unusual type of magma called kimberlite, which erupts at a type of volcanic vent called a diatreme or pipe.*

▲ *Pumice rocks are igneous rocks formed when the lava cools quickly above the ground. The rocks are very light and porous.*

Geysers and Hot Springs

Apart from erupting vents, the areas around volcanoes have other interesting features as well. These include hot springs and water geysers. Mud pots are formed when the heated water is mixed with mud and clay over the vent. The gases trying to escape through the vent causes the mud pot to bubble. If the hot water reaches the surface only in the form of steam, it is called a fumarole.

Hot Springs

Hot springs are gushes of hot water that are found on land. These are formed when molten materials deep in the Earth cool down, giving off water vapour. The hot vapour moves up through cracks in the rocks, cooling down in the process. Gradually it condenses to become water and bubbles forth from the ground.

Rich in Mineral

The water from hot springs is clear and rich in mineral content. The minerals are dissolved from the rocks as the water moves up from deep in the Earth. Countries such as Japan, New Zealand, Kenya and Iceland are well known for hot springs.

▲ *The water in hot springs often boils, giving off steam which we see as bubbles on the surface. The Crested Pool at Yellowstone National Park, US, is one such hot spring.*

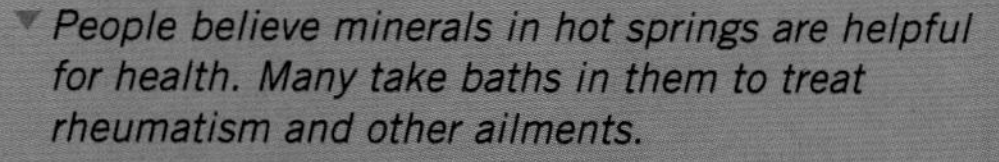

▼ *People believe minerals in hot springs are helpful for health. Many take baths in them to treat rheumatism and other ailments.*

Natural Fountains

Geysers are nature's own fountains of water wherein a vent at the surface regularly throws up jets of hot water and steam. Scientists believe these are created when water enters cavities deep inside the Earth's surface and interacts with rocks heated by magma.

INTERESTING FACT

Geysers and hot springs are also formed from submarine volcanoes. Water percolates down through cracks in the rocks in the mid-ocean ridge, moving towards the sea floor. There the water is superheated before gushing out from vents at temperatures of 300°C to 400°C.

FACT FILE

- Highest geyser at present - Steamboat Geyser, at Norris Geyser Basin, Yellowstone National Park, US
  Height: 116 metres (380 feet)
- Highest ever - Waimangu Geyser, New Zealand, before it was wiped out by landslides in 1904
  Height: Over 300 metres (1,000 feet)

▼ *Geysers usually discharge hot water and steam up to heights of 50 metres (164 feet), but at times can even reach 500 metres (1,640 feet).*

Shooting Up

The heat from the molten rocks boils water and the high pressure builds up bubbles of steam. Finally, the pressure is strong enough to explosively shoot out the water and steam through a vent. This cycle can be repeated regularly.

▶ *Fumaroles are weak geysers that vent out volcanic gases through fissures, such as sulphur vapour.*

Extraterrestrial Volcanoes

Earth is not the only place where volcanoes occur. Scientists have observed proof of volcanic activities on the Earth's Moon and other planets of the solar system. Volcanoes on the Moon and planets such as Mars and Venus are nearly three to four billion years old.

Sea of Lava

The Earth's Moon has no large volcanoes like the Hawaiian ones or Mount St Helens in the United States. However, vast parts of the lunar surface are covered with lava. The earliest astronomers mistook these to be water and called them 'maria' or 'mare' (Latin for 'sea').

Quiet Flow

There are no violent volcanic eruptions on the Moon due to a lack of dissolved water and reduced gravity. The lunar maria shows some small volcanic domes and cones, but these are largely flat and comprise broad, slim layers around the vents. Since the Moon's gravity is less than Earth's, the lava is more fluid and flows out easily and quietly over large areas.

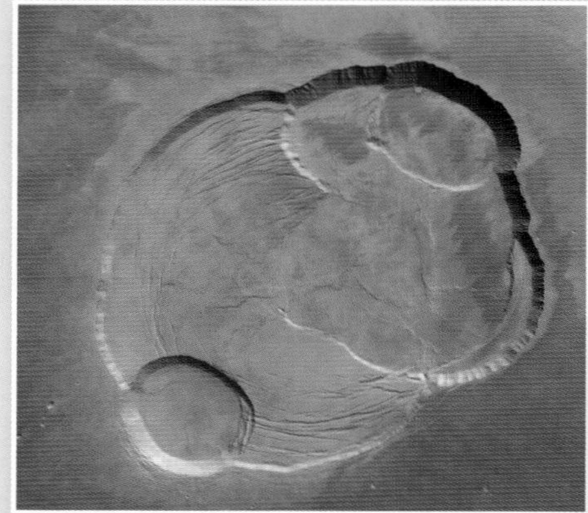

▲ *The largest volcano on Mars, Olympus Mons, is a circular structure that would span the entire Hawaiian island chain on Earth.*

▼ *Galileo was an unmanned spacecraft sent by NASA to study the planet Jupiter and its moons. The Galileo probe images revealed active volcanoes on Jupiter's moon Io.*

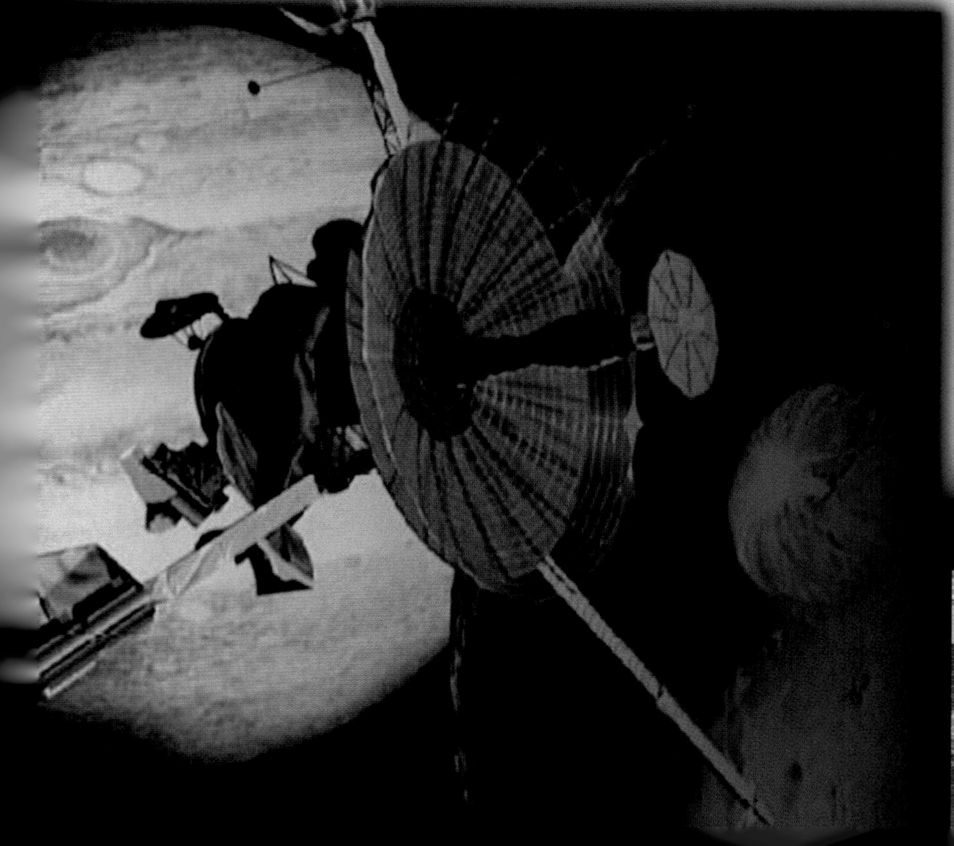

Largest Shield Volcanoes

Mars has the largest shield volcanoes in the solar system, though the numbers are few. The 'red planet' also has large volcanic cones, mare-like volcanic plains and other smaller features. However, there are hardly any active volcanoes on Mars today.

Most Numbers

Venus has more volcanoes than any other planet in the solar system. No one can be sure about how many there are, and the total could be over a million. Most volcanoes on Venus are shield volcanoes, but there are some unusual ones as well. Again, it cannot be proved beyond doubt that the volcanoes are no longer active.

▼ *Volcano eruptions on Venus involve fluid lava flows. There are no signs of any explosive, ash-forming eruptions.*

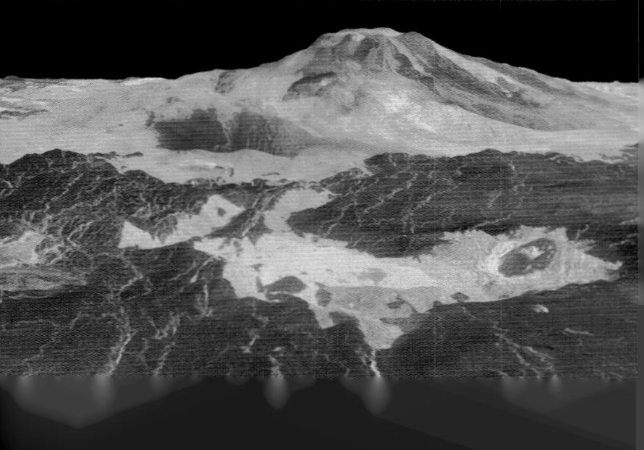

Famous Volcanoes

There are more than 500 active volcanoes on Earth's surface, which are known to have erupted at least once in recorded history and some of these have gained fame for various reasons.

▼ *In 1748, a peasant chanced upon a buried brick wall, and excavations of Pompeii began. About three-quarters of Pompeii has now been uncovered. Visitors can see buildings as they stood almost 2,000 years ago.*

Vesuvius

Mt Vesuvius is a volcano east of Naples, Italy. One of the most violent explosions on Vesuvius occurred in AD 79, completely destroying the ancient Roman cities of Pompeii and Herculaneum. It has erupted many times since then and is regarded as one of the most dangerous volcanoes in the world.

▲ *The violent eruption of Mount St Helens in 1980 blew the top of the mountain off, reducing its summit by 400 metres (1,312 feet) and replacing it with a horseshoe-shaped crater.*

St Helens

Mount St Helens is an active volcano in Washington, US. The first recorded eruption was in 1800, while the most devastating one took place in 1980. The latter killed 57 people and thousands of animals, and destroyed over 200 homes. The eruption lasted over nine hours.

▲ *Mauna Loa is among the most active volcanoes on Earth. It has erupted 33 times since its first recorded eruption in 1843. The most recent one was in 1984.*

Mauna Loa

Mauna Loa is the largest active volcano on Earth and makes up nearly half of the island Hawaii. It is an active shield volcano that erupted last in 1984. In Hawaiian, 'mauna loa' means 'long mountain'.

Mount Etna

Mount Etna is an active volcano on the east coast of Sicily. It is the highest volcano in Europe and has the longest history of recorded eruptions.

INTERESTING FACT

In AD 79, Mt Vesuvius was thought to be extinct – its crater being covered with vegetation. As a result, its eruption took the cities by surprise. Pompeii and Herculaneum were so thoroughly covered that ruins of the cities remained uncovered for nearly 1,700 years.

FACT FILE

- Mt Etna: Highest summit over 3,200 metres (10,000 feet) high; base of about 150 km (93 miles)
- Mt St Helens: About 2,550 metres (8,363 feet) high
- Mt Vesuvius cone: Currently 1,281 metres (4,203 feet) high
- Mauna Loa: About 4,170 metres (13,681 feet) high

More Famous Volcanoes

Volcanoes inspire feelings of awe in most people, but there is more to the phenomenon than just fire and fury, or lava and ash. This is the reason why volcanoes have been an object of curiosity and interest among both scientists and everyday people.

Mt Fuji

Mount Fuji is the highest mountain in Japan. Surrounded by the Five Lakes, it is also one of the most scenic of all volcanoes. The volcano is designated as active, though with low risk of eruption. The last recorded eruption occurred in 1707.

▲ *The famous cone-shaped, active Mt Fuji volcano in Japan remains completely buried in snow in the winter.*

Kilauea

Kilauea is one of the world's most active volcanoes, with lava flowing almost continuously. Eruptions at Kilauea happen both from the summit and along the lengthy east and southwest rift zones that extend to the sea.

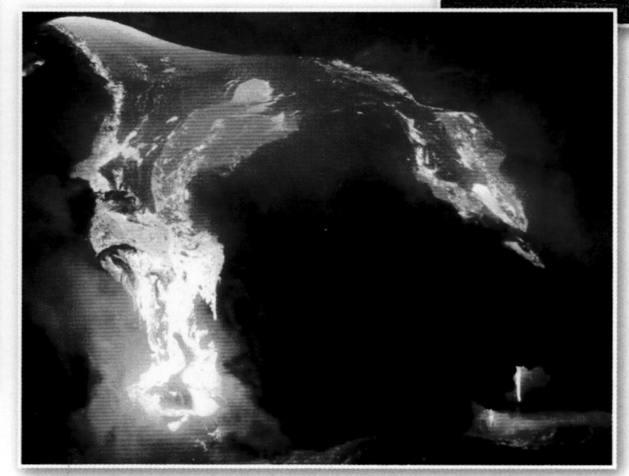

▲ *Lava flow from a volcanic eruption can travel for miles before it cools down and becomes solid. Everything that gets in the way of the hot lava gets knocked down or burnt. But since the lava flows slowly, people can usually get out of its way in good time.*

▲ *Kilauea in the Hawaii Island is famed for its frequent eruptions, though most of these are confined within the crater. Some of its major violent explosions were recorded in 1955, 1975 and 1983.*

Stromboli

Stromboli has one of the longest recorded periods of activity. It is a small island in the Tyrrhenian Sea, Italy. For at least the last 2,000 years, it has been erupting almost continually.

Mt Rainier

Mount Rainier is located in Pierce County, in Washington, US Rainier is mostly covered by glaciers. It is a famous destination for winter sports, including snowshoeing and skiing. The most recent eruption was over 175 years ago.

◀ *For generations, Mt Rainier was known as Takhoma or Tahoma. But on May 8, 1792, Captain George Vancouver of the British Royal Navy officially named it after his friend, Rear Admiral Peter Rainier!*

INTERESTING FACT

Indonesia has had the most active volcanoes in recorded time – as many as 76. These volcanoes have recorded a total of 1,171 eruptions, which have caused a large number of fatalities.

FACT FILE

- Mt Rainier: Above 4,392 metres (14,410 feet)
- Mt Fuji: 3,776 metres (12,388 feet)
- Stromboli: 900 metres (2,900 feet)
- Kilauea: 1,222 metres (4,009 feet) at the summit

Volcanology

The study of volcanoes is called volcanology, and the people who study the science are called volcanologists. A volcanologist's job is exciting and adventurous. To become a volcanologist, one needs to study maths and science in high school, and geology in college or at university!

Predicting Eruptions

A volcanologist's main job is to predict volcanic eruptions. Little can be done to stop property damage in the surrounding areas when a volcano explodes, but many lives can be saved if people are located to a safe place before the eruption begins.

▲ *The HUGO underwater observatory monitors the Loihi submarine volcano, off Hawaii. The project, begun in 1997, aims to study underwater volcanism.*

Instruments Used

Volcanologists use different instruments to predict an eruption. A tiltmeter is used to measure the expansion of a volcano indicating the rising or lowering of magma levels. A device called a seismograph helps in detecting earthquakes caused by magma. Thermometers check for temperature rises in the area, while gas detectors measure the quantity of gas escaping.

◀ *Geologist measuring the height of a lava fountain at an eruption of the Kilauea volcano in 1983.*

▶ *Volcanologists use a special type of thermometer called a thermocouple for measuring the temperature of lava.*

Dangerous Mission

Volcanologists must follow strict safety measures since they may be required to work near erupting volcanoes. Observatories have been set up on the slopes or rims of several volcanoes, among them Mount Asama in Japan, Kilauea in Hawaii, and Vesuvius in Italy. The Alaska observatory keeps track of the 100 active volcanoes in the region.

Death on Duty

Maurice and Katia Krafft were famous volcanologists who studied and photographed erupting volcanoes all over the world. They were killed by a hot ash flow while photographing the eruption of Unzen in Japan in 1991.

▲ *The Hawaiian Volcano Observatory (HVO) is perched on the rim of the Kilauea caldera. It was set up in 1912.*

▼ *Volcanologists wear an outfit similar to a spacesuit, along with a helmet and gloves. The suit helps them survive the hot temperatures near erupting volcanoes.*

INTERESTING FACT

Some volcanoes, such as those in Hawaii, are easier to predict due to certain indications. Before such a volcano erupts, the surface expands slightly as magma collects in the magma chamber. As the magma travels up, several small earthquakes occur while the surrounding areas experience rising temperatures. Also, clouds of gas escape from the vents.

FACT FILE

MOST ACTIVE VOLCANOES

- Etna, Italy: About 3,500 years
- Stromboli, Italy: About 2,000 years
- Yasur, Vanuatu: About 800 years
- Ambrym, Vanuatu: Since 1774, when it was sighted by Captain Cook
- Tinakula, Solomon Islands: Reportedly since 1951

Volcanoes and the Weather

The Earth has witnessed gradual climate changes over the years. Many factors have led to these changes, and one factor among them is volcanic eruptions.

Small Outbursts

Minor eruptions take place around the world on an almost daily basis. In such cases volcanic ash, made up of rock and glass, is thrown high into the atmosphere. But this has little or no effect on the weather. It is the large eruptions that have a bigger effect on the climate patterns of the Earth.

▶ *Volcanic ash can be ejected to heights of many thousands of feet. The gases in the ash can create a haze in the upper layer of the atmosphere and affect global climate patterns.*

▲ *When hot lava enters the ocean, white-plume clouds are created by the heat and chemical reactions.*

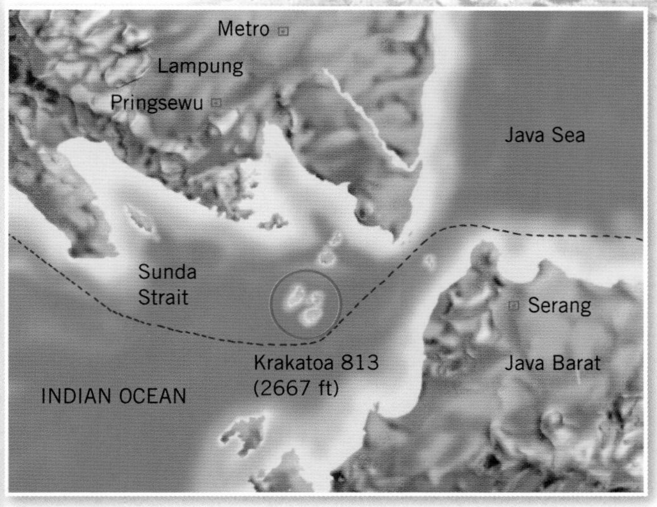

◀ *When the Krakatoa erupted in 1883, the entire northern portion of the island was blown away.*

▼ *According to one theory, dinosaurs disappeared from the Earth due to volcanic eruptions. Over a period of several million years, volcanoes could have created enough dust and soot to block out sunlight. As a result, food became scarce and temperatures changed. Some scientists believe dinosaurs could not adapt and so died out.*

Aerosol Effect

Volcanic ash is made up of particles and gases including sulphur dioxide. In the high atmosphere, the sulphur dioxide converts into aerosols. These aerosols in turn reflect the Sun's radiation back into outer space, and so less sunlight reaches the Earth's surface. This leads to the cooling of surface temperatures.

Krakatoa Volcano

After the eruption of Krakatoa in Indonesia in 1883, the volcanic dust was spread around the upper atmosphere by the jet streams. It is believed that world temperatures fell by an estimated 1.2°C.

Slowing Down

Nonetheless, even larger volcanic eruptions can have only a short-term effect on the Earth's climate, lasting perhaps a decade or so. Such eruptions will, at the most, only slow down the current trend of global warming rather than permanently halt it.

Earthquakes

Various disturbances beneath the Earth's surface cause the ground to jolt or shake. This is called an earthquake. A strong earthquake can shake many things, including buildings and bridges.

Fault Lines

Most earthquakes occur along a fault, which is a line or lines of fracture between plates of rocks on the Earth's crust. As the tectonic plates move, they collide, move apart, or slide past one another, often causing jolts. The presence of faults allow the rocks to shift relative to each other – one of the major factors behind earthquakes.

▲*The San Andreas Fault in California is the point where the Pacific Plate and the North American Plate move against each other.*

▲*Depending on the violence of ground movement, earthquakes can cause heavy damage to man-made structures like buildings, railways, bridges and dams.*

High Stress

Over a period of time, plate movement of the Earth causes large stresses to occur along a fault line. When the stress becomes too great, the resultant sudden release of energy due to the plates sliding, causes an earthquake.

Epicentre

The point on the Earth's surface directly above the focus is the epicentre of the quake. The strongest shaking is usually felt near the epicentre.

Primary Focus

The point within the Earth where the rocks first break or shift is called the focus or hypocentre of the quake. The focus of most earthquakes lies around 70 kilometres (43 miles) beneath the surface, though the deepest can be at 700 kilometres (435 miles).

▼*The focus is the point of sudden movement inside the Earth where an earthquake occurs. The shock waves then travel towards the ground surface.*

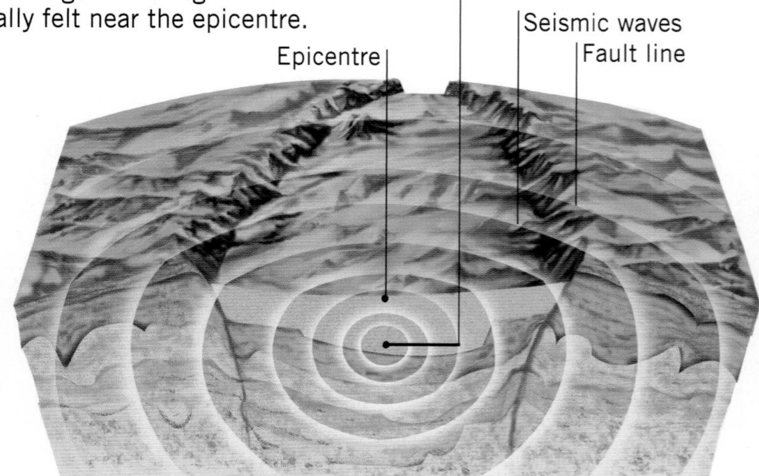

INTERESTING FACT

In an earthquake, the sudden movement releases energy. This energy travels through the Earth in the form of seismic waves. The waves move out from the focal point or epicentre of an earthquake in all directions and become weaker as they get farther away.

Famous Earthquakes

Earthquakes rarely ever kill people directly. Instead, the deaths and injuries are caused by the collapse of man-made structures like buildings, bridges and houses, or by fires from broken gas lines or flooding. There is also danger from rockfalls and falling trees or tree branches.

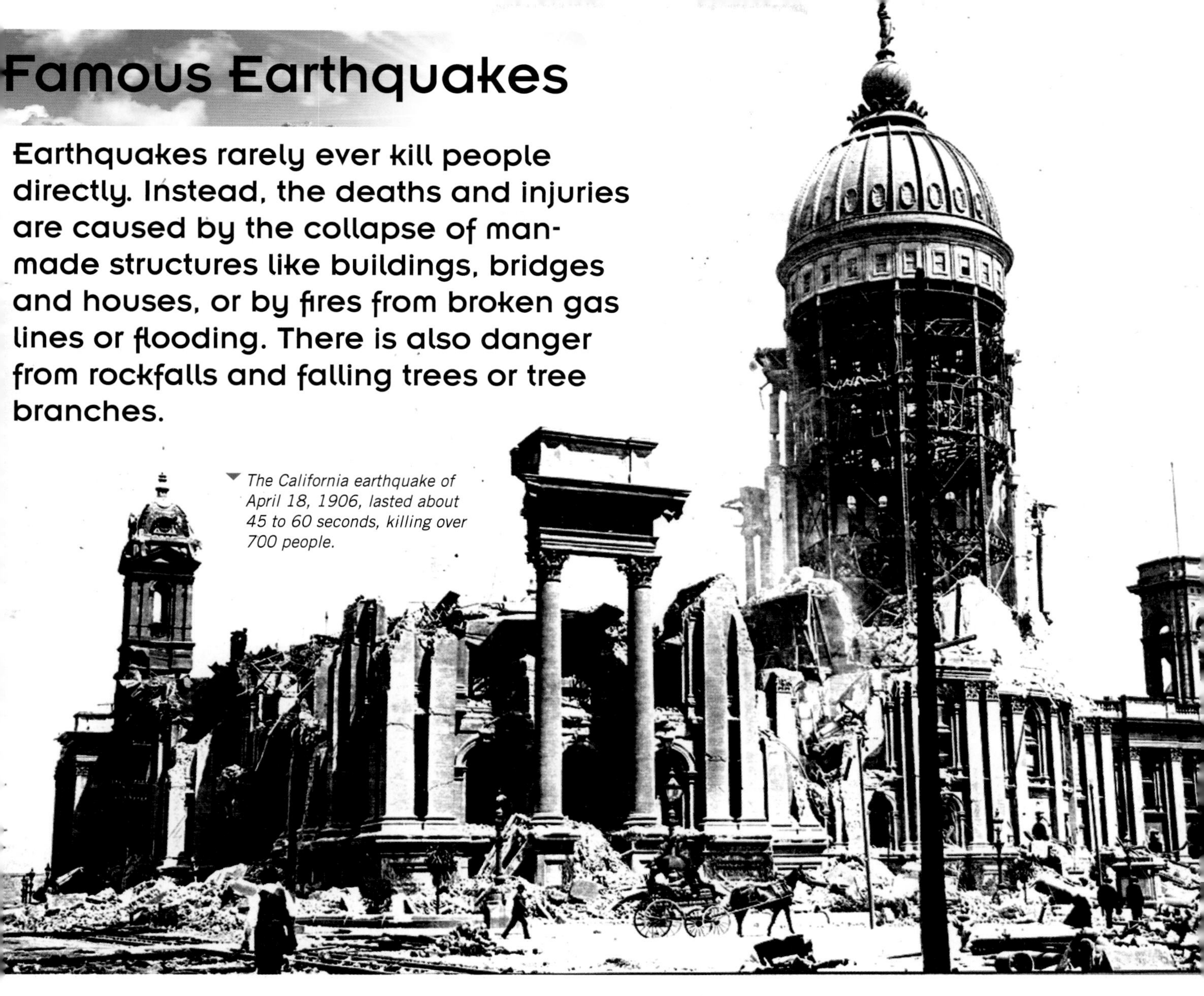

The California earthquake of April 18, 1906, lasted about 45 to 60 seconds, killing over 700 people.

Fire Hazard

A major cause of death and property damage with earthquakes, is fire. The 1906 San Francisco earthquake ranks as one of the worst disasters in American history because of a fire that raged for three days in the aftermath.

Chilean Quake

The Great Chilean Earthquake of May 22, 1960, is the largest earthquake in recorded history. The earthquake originated along the southern Chilean coast and caused a tsunami that hit Hawaii and the coastal areas of South America. About 3,000 people were killed in the earthquake/tsunami.

More than 90 percent of the deaths during the 1964 earthquake in Alaska were due to the tsunamis that hit the coast after the quake.

Japan Hit

The Great Kanto Earthquake in Japan, on September 1, 1923, caused huge destruction. Over one hundred thousand people were killed in the quake, which had a magnitude of 7.9 on the Richter scale. More than 88 fires broke out due to the quake.

▼ *The Great Kanto Earthquake that shook Tokyo and Yokohama in Japan in 1923, left a trail of destructive fires.*

Most deadly

The world's deadliest earthquake on record occurred in central China in 1556. Most people in the region lived in caves carved from soft rock. As the caves collapsed during the earthquake, an estimated 830,000 people lost their lives.

INTERESTING FACT

After the Chilean earthquake in 1960, seismographs recorded shock waves that travelled around the Earth. These waves caused the Earth to vibrate for many days afterwards! This phenomenon is described as the 'free oscillation of the Earth'.

FACT FILE

MOST DEVASTATING

- China, 1556: Magnitude 8; Over 830,000 dead
- China, 1976: Magnitude 7.8; Over 270,000 dead
- Syria, 1138: Over 230,000 dead
- China, 1927: Magnitude 8.3; Over 200,000 dead

▶ *The earthquake that struck San Fernando on February 9, 1971, ranks as one of the worst in the history of California. Measuring 6.5 on the Richter scale, the calamity caused the deaths of over 60 persons and extensive property damage.*

Measuring Earthquakes

While an earthquake cannot be predicted accurately, scientists are able to measure its intensity. They can also accurately pinpoint its epicentre and hypocentre.

Richter Scale

The most common reference for measuring earthquake intensity is the Richter scale. It was developed in 1935 by seismologists Beno Gutenberg of Germany and Charles F. Richter of the United States. The scale is a series of numbers from 1 to 10, and each increase in number is an increase by a factor of 10 in shaking amplitude.

Chinese philosopher Chang Hêng invented the earliest known seismoscope in AD 132. It resembled a wine jar about six feet in diameter. On the outside it had eight dragon heads facing the eight principal directions of the compass. During an earthquake, one of the dragon mouths would release a ball, depending on the direction of the shaking.

Increasing Intensity

Every increase of one number in magnitude means the actual energy release of the quake is 32 times greater. For example, an earthquake of magnitude 7.0 releases 32 times more energy than an earthquake measuring 6.0.

INTERESTING FACT

An earthquake measuring 2 on the Richter scale can hardly be felt. On the other hand, a quake with magnitude greater than 7.0 may destroy many buildings.

FACT FILE

TOP 5 EARTHQUAKES

- Chile, 1960, 9.5 on the Richter scale
- Alaska, 1964, 9.2 on the Richter scale
- Alaska, 1957, 9.1 on the Richter scale
- Kamchatka, 1952, 9.0 on the Richter scale
- Northern Sumatra, 2004, 9.0 on the Richter scale

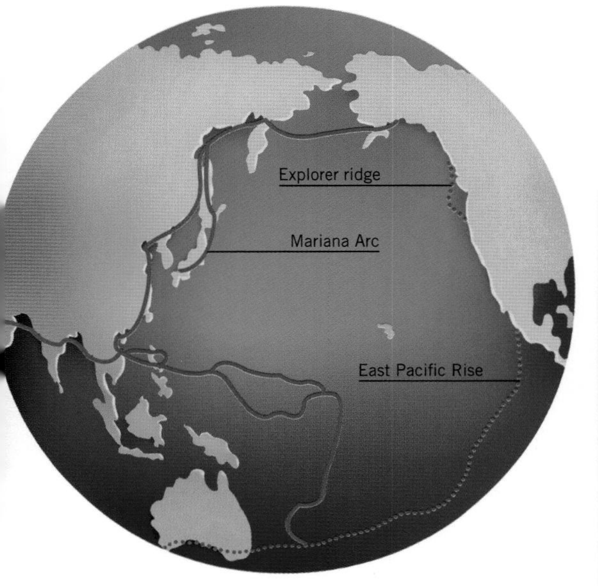

About 80 percent of the world's major earthquakes happen along a belt encircling the Pacific Ocean, called the Ring of Fire.

Seismic Measure

The strength and location of an earthquake is recorded using an instrument known as a seismograph. It has sensors called seismometers that can detect movements in the ground.

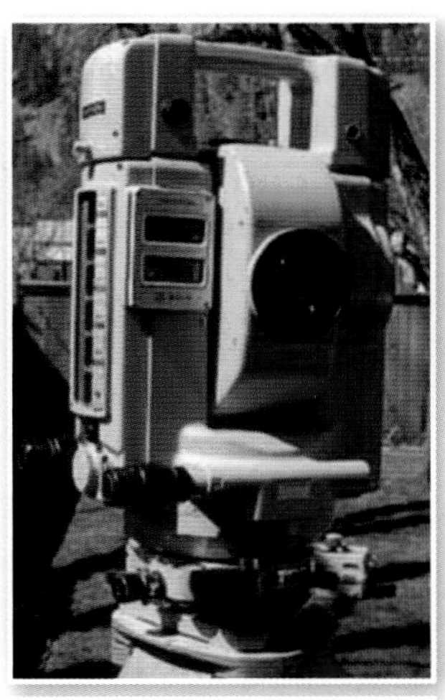

The instruments at Honolulu geophysical observatory monitor tidal levels at remote sites throughout the Pacific Basin. These are used to warn about tsunamis.

Scientists use the geodimeter to monitor changes on the Earth's surface near faults over a period of time. Thereby they hope to predict an earthquake with more accuracy.

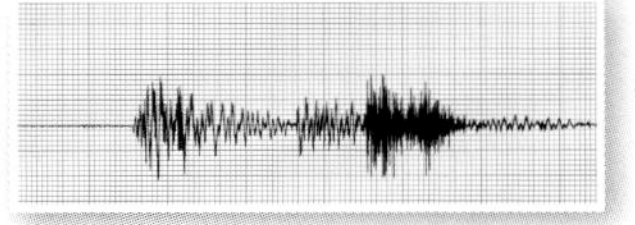

The zigzag line made by a seismograph is called a seismogram. It shows the changing intensity of the vibrations from an earthquake.

Features of Volcanoes and Earthquakes

Some earthquakes are caused by the movement of magma in volcanoes, and such quakes can be an early warning of volcanic eruptions. Earthquakes and volcanoes also give rise to phenomena like tsunamis, mudflows, ash flows and landslides.

Flow of Mud

Mudflows usually originate on volcanoes with large masses of ice and snow on their summits. They are caused by the speedy melting of a large amount of ice, caused by a volcanic eruption or due to an ice avalanche that has broken free because of an earthquake. These fast moving streams of mud sweep away everything in their path.

▼ *Earthquakes can trigger landslides that cause loss of life and great damage to property.*

Tsunami Crashes

Large earthquakes, and occasionally volcanic eruptions, beneath the ocean can create a series of huge, destructive waves called tsunamis that flood the coasts. Tsunamis gain in height when they reach shallow water near the shore.

◀ *Sometimes, volcanic ash combines with water and forms a boiling mudflow, which can be highly destructive.*

▲ *Before the tsunami hits the coast, the sea often recedes from the coast – like it did at the Kalutara Beach in Sri Lanka in 2004. If the slope is shallow, the withdrawal can exceed 800 metres (2,625 feet)*

Indian Ocean

On December 26, 2004, an earthquake of magnitude 9.0 in the Indian Ocean triggered a series of killer tsunamis. At least 160,000 people were killed, making it the deadliest tsunami in recorded history.

Caught Unawares

People who are unaware of the danger that accompanies a tsunami may often remain at the shore due to curiosity, or perhaps to collect fish when the sea withdraws before a tsunami. When the tsunami strikes with all its force, it is often too late for them to run.

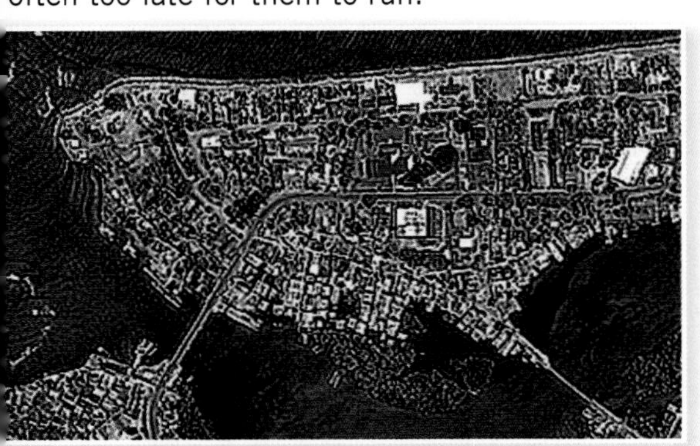

◀ *The tsunamis of 2004 caused widespread destruction in Aceh in Indonesia. This picture shows a calm coastline before December 26, 2004.*

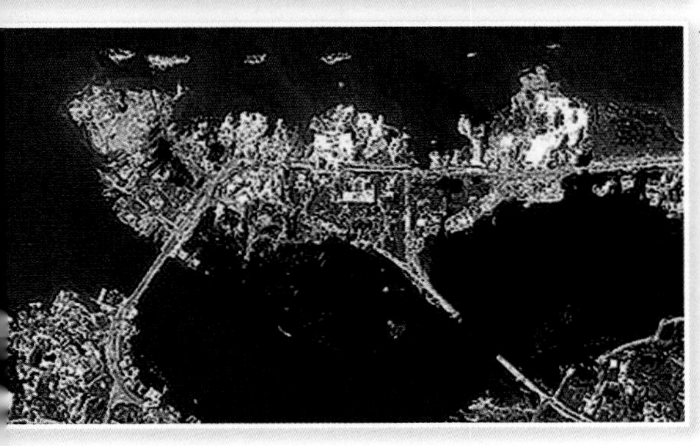

◀ *The tsunamis that struck the Indian Ocean in 2004 washed away everything in their way – roads, buildings, bridges and hundreds of thousands of people.*

INTERESTING FACT

Although both are sea waves, a tsunami and a tidal wave are completely different. A tidal wave is a large sea wave generated by high winds, while a tsunami is a sea wave caused by an underwater disturbance (usually triggered by an earthquake) displacing the ocean water.

FACT FILE

- Mudflow speed: Nearly 100 km (62 miles) per hour on steep slopes
- Tsunami height: Up to 30 metres (98 feet)
- Tsunami speed: Average of 800 to 970 km (497 to 603 miles per hour)
- The term 'tsunami' comes from the Japanese 'tsu' (harbour) and 'nami' (wave)

In Preparation

Earthquakes can strike any time, and foolproof warning systems have yet to be developed, so we must look to special building techniques and survival knowledge to protect ourselves.

Building Structures

Special building techniques in earthquake-prone areas can help reduce injury, loss of life, and property damage when disaster does strike. Earthquake resistant techniques include bolting buildings to their foundations and erecting support walls called shear walls.

The suspension bridge across the Tagus River in Lisbon, Portugal, was designed to withstand major earthquakes. One of its foundations was secured 79 metres (260 feet) deep under the water.

Fastened Down

In earthquake-resistant buildings such as homes, schools and workplaces, heavy appliances and furniture are fastened down to prevent them from falling over when the building shakes. Gas and water lines are purposefully laid with flexible joints to prevent leakage.

The Aftershocks

A large earthquake may be accompanied by many quakes of smaller magnitude. These later quakes are called aftershocks and can also cause immense damage. The safe option is to keep away from walls, windows, staircases and smashed structures that could fall.

▲ *If stuck indoors during an earthquake, the best safety measure is to take cover under a piece of heavy furniture and hold on to it, or simply stand against an inside wall.*

INTERESTING FACT

In the event of a major or even moderate earthquake, the frequency of aftershocks can go up to 1,000 or more in the course of a single day. Aftershocks can follow weeks and even months after the main earthquake.

FACT FILE

LARGEST EVACUATIONS BEFORE VOLCANIC ERUPTION

- Nyiragongo, 2002: About 500,000 evacuated in Congo
- Pinatubo, 1991: About 250,000 evacuated in the Philippines
- Galunggung, 1982: About 75,000 evacuated in Indonesia
- Mayon, 1984: About 73,000 evacuated in the Philippines

Evacuation

Unlike earthquakes, a volcano eruption can be predicted with more certainty. Once volcanologists warn of an eruption, the area around the volcano is evacuated. While damage to property cannot be avoided, lives can definitely be saved.

▶ *The Beehive Parliament House in New Zealand is just 400 metres (1,312 feet) from the Wellington fault zone, which is capable of causing big earthquakes. The building had to be rebuilt with new foundations, stronger walls and new beams. Specially made blocks of rubber and lead were placed between the foundations and the main beams.*

Rescue Mission

Relief and rescue efforts must be put in operation immediately after a disaster strikes. Rescue workers search for survivors in the aftermath of an earthquake or a volcanic eruption.

Honeycombed In

Collapsed buildings are like honeycombs with void spaces, which allow those trapped inside to survive. In the instance of the 1992 Philippines earthquake, a man was extracted with a broken ankle after 13 days trapped in a hotel that had collapsed during the event.

Miracles

Unusual survival stories are often termed as 'miracles'. The rescue team, however, know that such a possibility always exists. The team has to be careful and patient while digging through the rubble.

▶ *A rescue team waits for a building to be propped up, before entering. Buildings, weakened by earthquakes, can collapse long after the shock.*

▼ *People trapped in earthquake rubble stand a better chance of survival if they are rescued within 72 hours.*

The San Francisco earthquake on April 18, 1906, left a series of destruction. Several blocks of apartments were severely damaged and fires raged for days after the earthquake.

Hi-tech Search

Firefighters use a range of specialist devices to locate victims trapped within void spaces in collapsed structures. Such devices include fibre-optic and Ground Penetrating Radar technology, special search cameras, highly sensitive instruments for sensing sound and vibration, search dogs, and direct visual and voice contact.

Volcano Rescue Team

With volcano-watching becoming a favoured attraction for tourists, volcano rescue teams have been formed for any emergencies that may happen. These men are specially trained for rescue efforts on mountains.

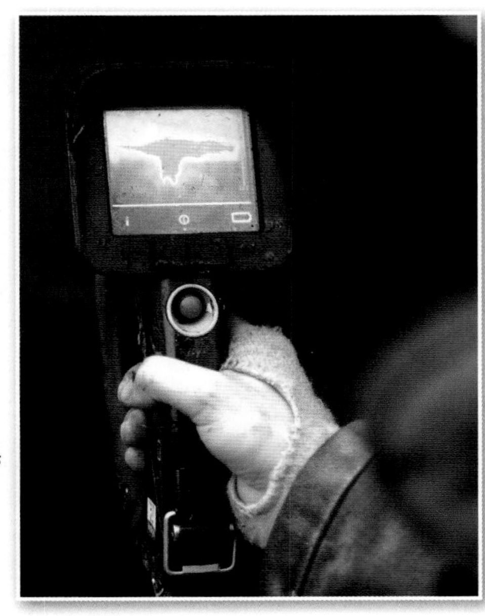

Earthquake rescue teams use thermal-imaging cameras to locate survivors trapped in the rubble.

INTERESTING FACT

A 97 year old woman in Bam has come to be regarded as the world's oldest and most famous earthquake survivor. She was found alive under the rubble nine days after an earthquake struck Iran on December 26, 2003.

FACT FILE

The International Committee of the Red Cross is the oldest of the world's rescue groups. It has been helping victims of wars and natural disasters for more than 100 years now.

Legends

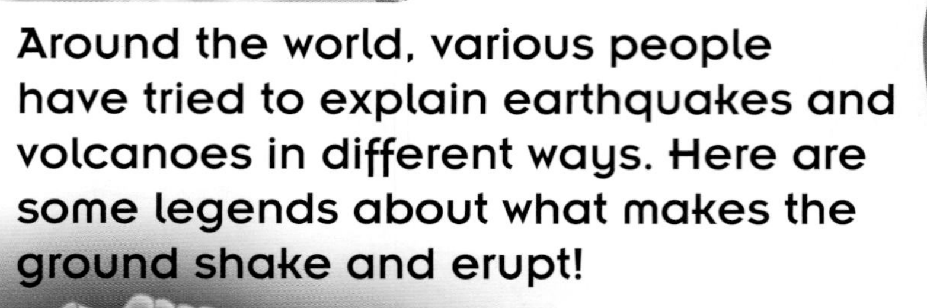

Around the world, various people have tried to explain earthquakes and volcanoes in different ways. Here are some legends about what makes the ground shake and erupt!

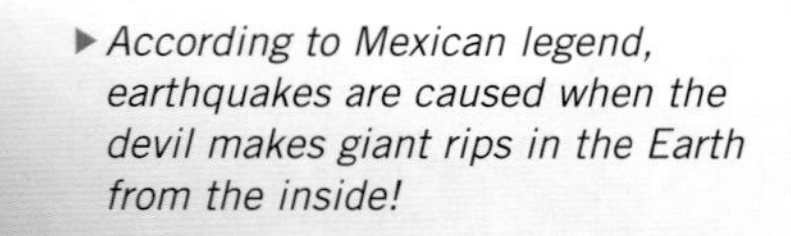

▸ *According to Mexican legend, earthquakes are caused when the devil makes giant rips in the Earth from the inside!*

◂ *The word 'volcano' comes from the island of Vulcano, off Sicily. Centuries ago, people there believed that Vulcano was the chimney of the god, Vulcan's forge.*

Devilish Moves

In Mexico, it was believed that El Diablo, the devil, made giant cuts in the Earth from the inside. Thus, he and his devilish mates could use the cracks to go up and carry out mischief on Earth whenever they wanted to.

Vulcan's Forge

People in Sicily believed that the lava fragments and dust clouds erupting from a volcano came from the god Vulcan's forge as he cut out thunderbolts for Jupiter, king of the gods, and weapons for Mars, the god of war. Vulcan was the god of fire in Roman religion.

Baby Ru

A legend in New Zealand has it that Mother Earth carries within her womb a child, the young god Ru. And every time he stretches and kicks – as babies do – an earthquake happens!

Greek Idea

In Greece, the philosopher Aristotle proposed that strong, unruly winds were trapped in underground caverns. As these winds thrashed about struggling to escape, earthquakes hit the Earth.

INTERESTING FACT

Legend describes Pele, the goddess of fire in Hawaiian religion, as an expert rider of the holua, a wooden sled that skates down steep slopes. Once, Papalauahi and other chiefs challenged Pele to a competition to judge who the best holua rider was. Papalauahi won the race. Pele, who was noted for her anger, produced a great flood of lava that swept away several of the chiefs and bystanders, creating lava trees out of them!

FACT FILE

Central American folklore relates that the square Earth is kept hoisted at its four corners by four gods. When the gods believe the Earth is becoming too crowded, they tilt it to get rid of the extra people.

▲ *Hawaiian people attributed volcanic activity to the beautiful but wrathful Pele, the goddess of fire. Whenever she was angry or spiteful, she made volcanoes erupt with fire!*

◄ *In the 4th century BC, Aristotle proposed that earthquakes were caused by winds trapped in caves beneath the ground.*

Fascinating Facts

Volcanoes are nature's 'fireworks display', while earthquakes occur when the Earth gets a bit 'shaken up'. While both cause large-scale damage, they are nonetheless very fascinating. In fact, tourists are known to visit volcanic areas in hopes of catching a glimpse of streaming lava or surging smoke.

Close Quarters

Volcanologists have ventured into the craters of some volcanoes. But nobody really goes all the way down, since it is too hot and filled with poisonous gases. One can only learn about the way volcanoes work by examining old craters.

Moonquakes

Moonquakes (tremors on the Moon's surface) have been observed, but their frequency is less than that of earthquakes. Also, moonquakes are generally much smaller in magnitude than the quakes here. Most moonquakes occur at great depth, about halfway between the surface and the centre of the Moon.

▼ Volcanologists have to sometimes explore inside a crater to collect rock and gas samples for study.

▼ Moonquakes were first discovered during the Apollo missions to the Moon. Moonquakes are much weaker than earthquakes, as the Moon's core is colder and has a solid mantle – unlike the Earth's molten core.

The Animal Sense

It is believed that animals can sense the onset of earthquakes, and that they start behaving strangely. Such changes in behaviour cannot, however, be used to predict earthquakes precisely, since a connection between a specific behaviour and the occurrence of an earthquake has not yet been made.

Alaska is one of the most earthquake prone areas in the world, with over 4,000 earthquakes recorded at various depths per year.

Man-made Quakes

Humans have also been responsible for causing earthquakes. The accumulation of large masses of water behind dams, digging of mines, injection of fluid into the Earth's crust, and detonation of huge bombs are some of our activities that can lead to earthquakes.

INTERESTING FACT

Alaska is the most earthquake prone state in the world. Earthquakes of magnitude 7 occur there almost every year, while those of magnitude 8 or larger, happen every 14 years on average.

FACT FILE

An earthquake of magnitude 5 may release energy 10,000 times as much as that of the first atomic bomb.

It is believed that animals can sense earthquakes beforehand. In 373 BC, for instance, rats, snakes and weasels deserted the Greek city of Helice in droves just days before a devastating earthquake struck.

What's the Weather Like?

When you look out of the house to see if it's a sunny, windy or rainy day, you are checking the weather. Weather is the state of the atmosphere or the air that surrounds the Earth at a particular time and location. It may be hot or cold, cloudy or clear, windy or calm.

Climatic Factor

Weather is not the same as climate. While weather is the condition of air over a short period – a few hours to a few days, climate is the average weather condition over a long time, usually 10-30 years.

Life Matters

Weather affects farming schedules. Farmers need clear weather to plant and harvest their crops. Plants need sunlight and rainfall to grow, but a storm or sudden frost can damage crops.

Grey or Chirpy

Changing weather affects our lives in many ways. We dress according to the weather, choosing heavy woollens when cold and dressing lightly if it is hot. Weather can even have an effect on our mood!

▼ *Planting of crops is dependent on weather conditions. In some countries, crops are planted only when rains are expected.*

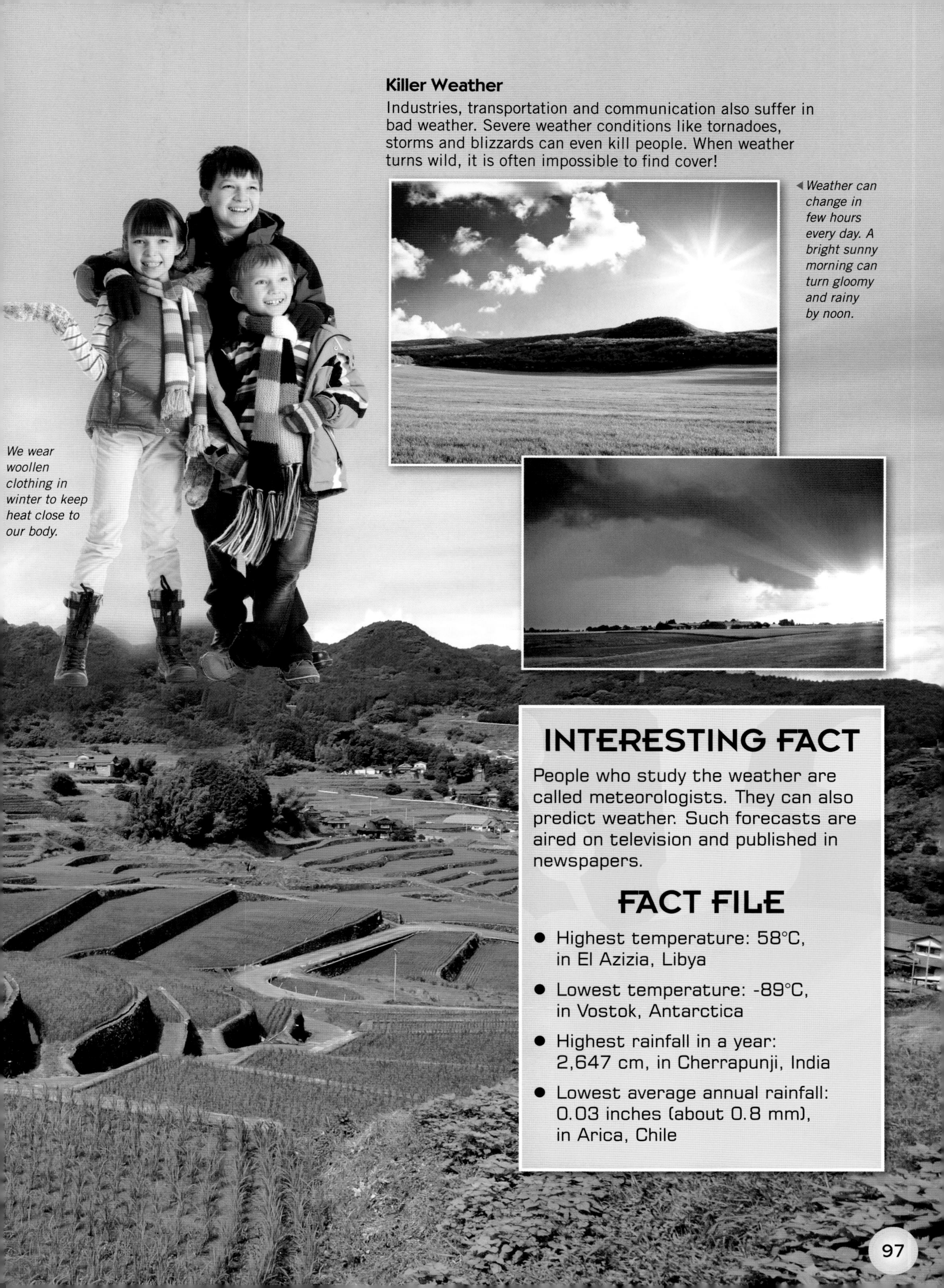

Killer Weather

Industries, transportation and communication also suffer in bad weather. Severe weather conditions like tornadoes, storms and blizzards can even kill people. When weather turns wild, it is often impossible to find cover!

Weather can change in few hours every day. A bright sunny morning can turn gloomy and rainy by noon.

We wear woollen clothing in winter to keep heat close to our body.

INTERESTING FACT

People who study the weather are called meteorologists. They can also predict weather. Such forecasts are aired on television and published in newspapers.

FACT FILE

- Highest temperature: 58°C, in El Azizia, Libya
- Lowest temperature: -89°C, in Vostok, Antarctica
- Highest rainfall in a year: 2,647 cm, in Cherrapunji, India
- Lowest average annual rainfall: 0.03 inches (about 0.8 mm), in Arica, Chile

Sun and Water

The conditions that influence the weather include wind, pressure, temperature, humidity, clouds and precipitation. Nearly all weather changes occur in the lowest layer of the atmosphere, called the troposphere.

Starting with the Sun

The Sun's energy heats certain parts of the Earth more than others. The unequal heating leads to variations in temperature, wind, air pressure and ocean currents. This causes weather changes.

Temperature Changes

Hot air is lighter than cold air. As air gets heated, it rises up and cold air rushes in to take its place. This causes wind, which can be as slow as a gentle breeze, or fast and raging like a fierce storm.

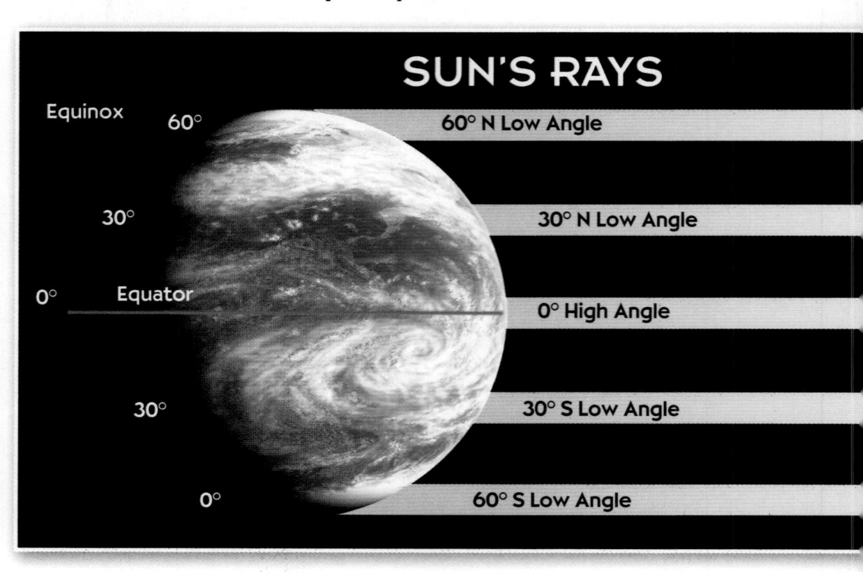

The Sun's rays fall directly overhead at the Equator, making it the hottest area. The North Pole and the South Pole are the coldest, since the Sun's rays strike them at an angle.

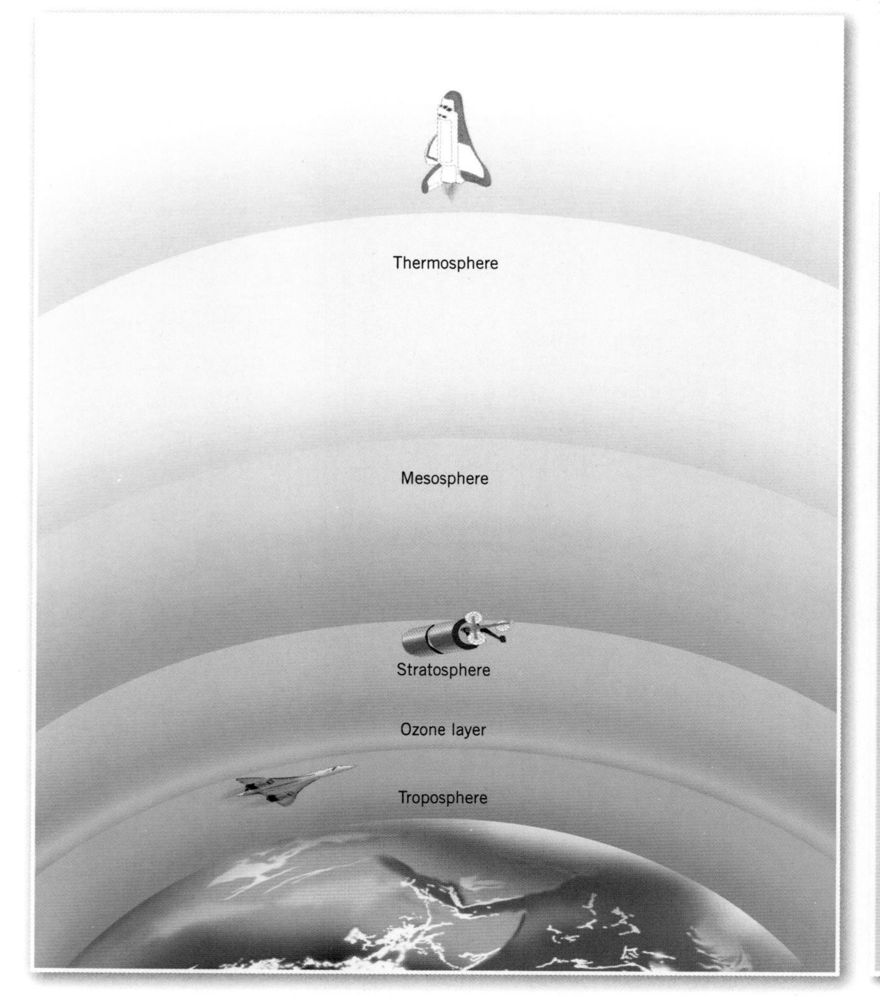

Apart from weather changes, the atmosphere also protects us from the Sun's harmful radiation.

INTERESTING FACT

Like Earth, the planet Mars also has an atmosphere. Observation has shown a variety of spectacular weather changes on Mars. These include pink skies, ice clouds, giant dust storms and cyclones.

FACT FILE

- On average, the Earth reflects 30 percent of the Sun's energy back to space. For the rest...
- Fresh snow reflects about 85 percent of the Sun's energy
- Dry soil reflects about 10 percent of the Sun's energy
- Clouds reflect upwards of 20 percent of the Sun's energy

Evaporating Water

The Sun also causes the water cycle – the process by which water circulates between land and air, forming clouds and rain. The Sun heats up water in rivers, lakes and oceans, and turns it into vapour. This is called evaporation.

The water cycle leads to rainfall, snow or sleet. This water returns back into rivers, lakes and oceans.

WATER CYCLE

Water storage in ice and snow
Precipitation
Water storage in the atmosphere
Condensation
Snow-melt runoff to streams
Transpiration
Evaporation
Water storage in ice and snow
Ground water infiltration
Ground water storage
Ground water storage
Ground water discharge
Surface runoff

ooling Off

s the water vapour rises, the air turns cold and the apour changes into tiny droplets, forming clouds. hen the droplets become too heavy, they fall in he form of rain, hail, sleet or snow. This continuous rocess makes up the water cycle.

▶ *Images from space telescopes show giant dust storms and cyclones on Mars. Wind speed during a dust storm on the planet can be over 200 kph. Mars has also been found to be cloudy and misty.*

Wind and Cloud

Wind and cloud are important elements of the weather. When air moves from areas of high pressure to ones of low pressure, it is known as wind. Clouds are formed when rising air cools as it can no longer hold all of its water vapour.

Naming by Direction

Some winds occur in a particular direction, and are named after the direction they blow from. An easterly wind blows from the east and a westerly wind blows from the west.

Gusty Winds

As a basic rule, the greater the pressure difference, the stronger the wind. Wind speeds are measured using an instrument called an anemometer.

◀ *Wind speed is measured by an instrument called the anemometer. The three 'cups' on it catch the wind, causing it to rotate. Anemometers should be placed about nine metres (30 feet) above the ground.*

▶ *Wind speeds can vary greatly, from gentle evening breezes to tearaway storms. The higher the pressure difference, the more powerful the wind.*

INTERESTING FACT

In the desert, temperatures can rise to extreme levels, producing short-lived whirlwinds. Such winds form a spiralling column of hot air and rarely last for more than a few minutes.

FACT FILE

- A sea breeze can cause an 8°C to 11°C drop in temperature in 30 minutes
- Highest wind speed: 372 kph, measured at Mt Washington
- Whirlwind height: More than 100 metres (330 feet)
- Windiest place: Commonwealth Bay, Antarctica Coast. Wind speeds there reach 119 kph
- Cirrus clouds are formed at the high levels - 9,144 metres (30,000 feet) or more

Clouded In

Clouds are formed when water vapour condenses to form of tiny droplets. They can be white, light grey or dark in colour, and come in various shapes and sizes. Wispy clouds are called cirrus and fluffy ones are known as cumulus. Clouds that appear in layers are stratus clouds. There are 10 types of clouds, each defined by height at which they occur and their shape.

Rain Bearer

Not all clouds are rain-bearing. Clouds that have the word 'nimbus' at the beginning or the end of their name, are rain clouds. Typically, cumulonimbus clouds are the most dangerous. They can cause hail, lightning, tornadoes, downdraughts, downbursts and flash floods.

TYPES OF CLOUDS

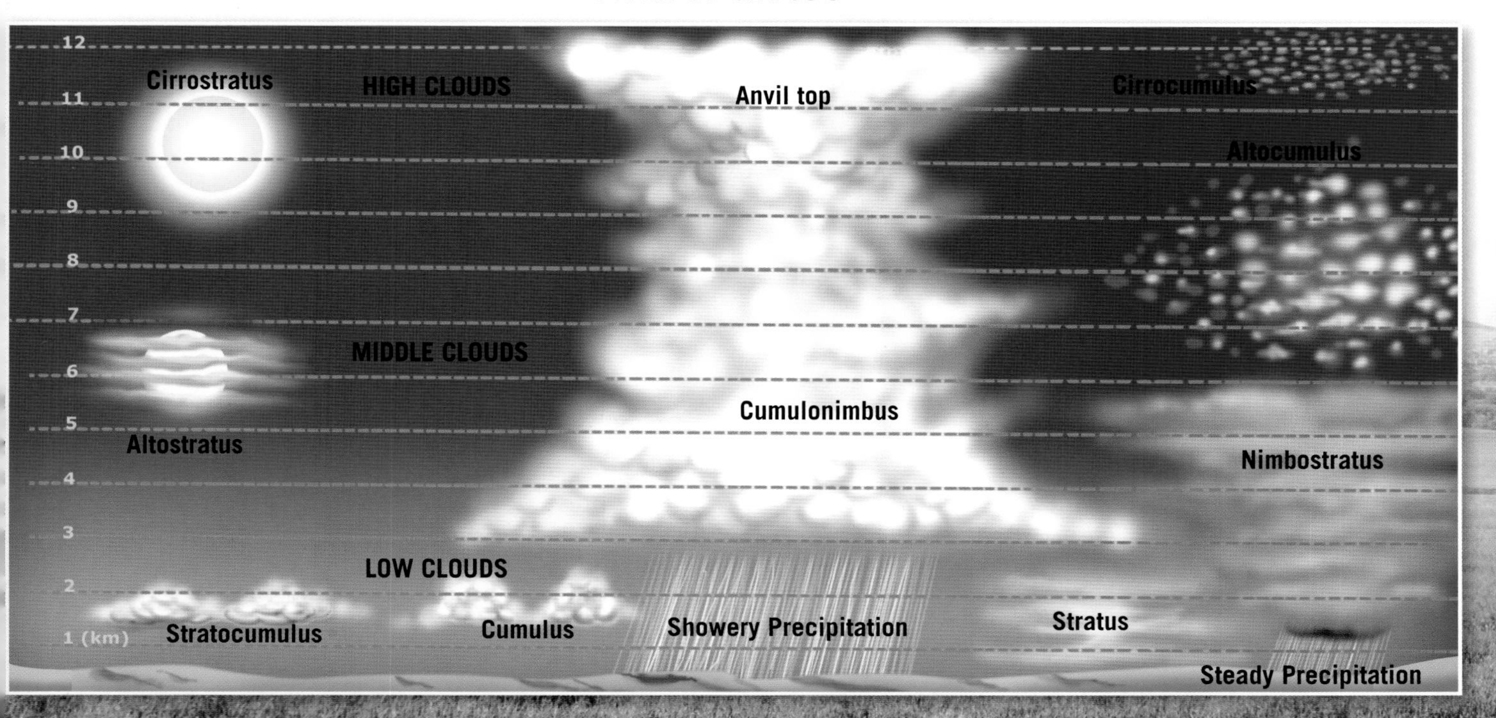

Seasons

Each of the four seasons – spring, summer, autumn and winter – has generally different weather conditions. Seasons occur due to the Earth's tilted axis as it goes around the Sun. The regions tilted towards the Sun have summer, while those tilted away, experience winter.

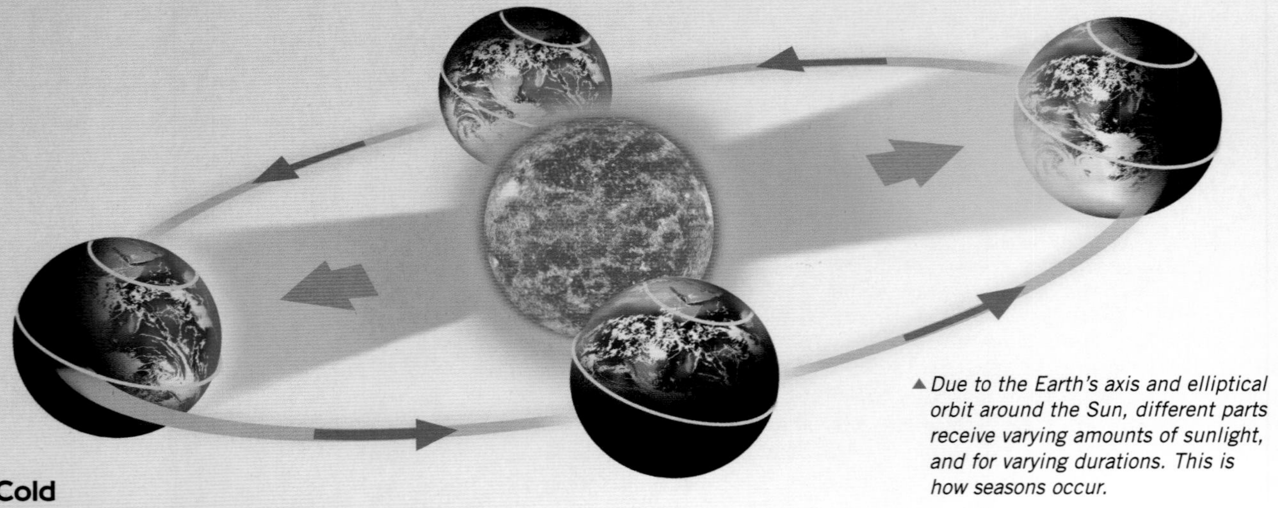

▲ *Due to the Earth's axis and elliptical orbit around the Sun, different parts receive varying amounts of sunlight, and for varying durations. This is how seasons occur.*

Hot and Cold

In the spring, days get warmer in the Northern Hemisphere. Summer follows, with hot days and warm nights. In autumn the days become cooler, gradually leading to a cold winter. When the Northern Hemisphere experiences winter, the Southern has its summer.

Four or Two

Some regions on Earth do not witness all four seasons. In the tropics, temperatures change only slightly. But the amount of rainfall varies, and these regions have wet and dry seasons. The polar areas have light and dark seasons. The sun shines almost all the time in summer, and it's continually dark during winter.

Extreme Conditions

Summer is the warmest season of the year, while winter is the coldest. Polar winters are freezing, while summers in desert regions can rise above 50 degrees Celsius!

▶ *The polar region gets sunlight only during the summer season. Winters are long, dark and bitterly cold.*

▶ *Changing weather conditions indicate the beginning of a new season. As autumn draws to a close, daily temperatures fall steadily to signal the onset of winter.*

Climates

The weather of a certain region over a long period of time is known as its climate. An area's climate determines the kinds of plants and animals that can survive there. The study of climate is called climatology.

▼ *Desert climates are marked by extremely hot days and cold nights and, usually, strong winds.*

Latitudinal Point

The Sun plays a crucial role in a region's climate. A region's latitude, or position north or south of the Equator, determines the angle at which the Sun's rays will strike. This creates different climatic conditions.

▶ *People who live in cold, snowy areas often use skis, sleds or snowmobiles for transportation.*

The houses people live in are also made to suit an area's climate. In rainy places, houses may have a steep, pointed roof so that the rainwater can drain off easily.

Other Factors

Regions with the same latitude may have different climates, depending on other factors. For instance, the inland area of a continent may be warmer in summer than the coast, which is cooled by the ocean air. Mountainous regions may also have a different climate.

Types of climate

World climates can be divided in many ways. Five broad groups are: tropical, dry, warm temperate, cold temperate and cold. Each of these is often further divided into subgroups.

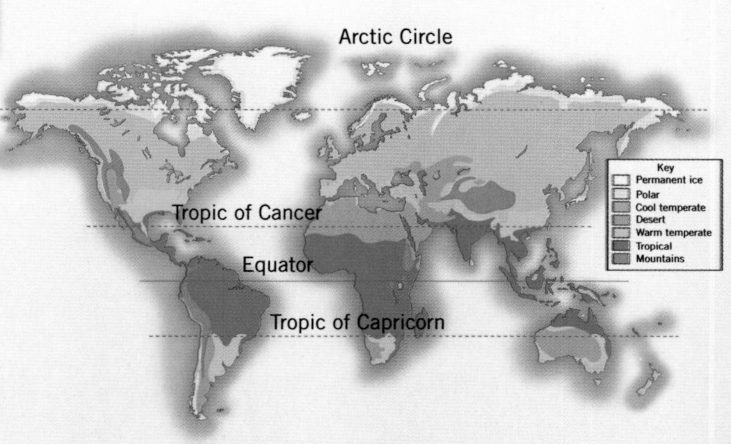

Broad Classifications

Areas with tropical climates are warm throughout the year, with no winters, whilst areas with cold climates face long and severe winters. Desert areas have dry climates, with little or no rainfall, whilst warm temperate areas have warm and wet summers and mild winters. Cold temperate climates are characterised by less extreme temperatures and frequent rainfall.

Humid and Hot

Extreme heat can be a life-threatening condition even though it is not as dramatic as other forms of severe weather. Heat waves often affect wide geographical areas and large numbers of people.

Heat waves can lead to fatal heatstrokes if precautions are not taken.

Relative Values

Relative humidity refers to the amount of moisture the air can hold before it rains. The most it can hold is 100 percent. Relative humidity in desert areas can be as low as 20 percent.

Humidity Factor

The amount of water vapour in the air is called humidity. The more moisture there is in the air, the higher the humidity. The amount of moisture that the air can hold depends on its temperature. Cooler air holds less moisture.

The best way to tackle a heat wave is to stay in the shade and drink lots of water.

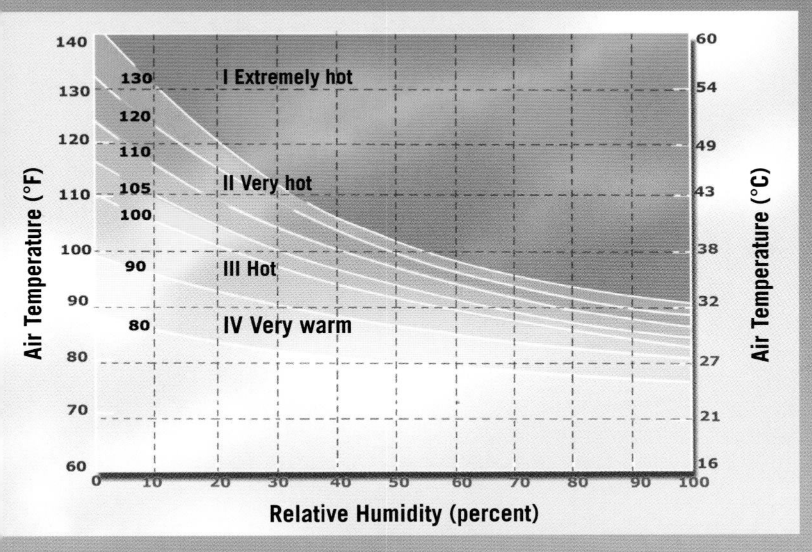

Extreme Danger (130 °F or higher): Heatstroke or sunstroke likely

Danger (105-129 °F): Sunstroke,muscle cramps and/or heat exhaustion likely. Heatstroke possible with prolonged exposure and/or physical activity

Extreme Caution (90-105 °F): Sunstroke, muscle cramps and/or heat exhaustion possible with prolonged exposure and/or physical activity

Caution (80-90 °F): Fatigue possible with prolonged exposure and/or physical activity

INTERESTING FACT

On calm, clear nights, the air just above the ground cools rapidly. If the temperature of this air falls below the dew point, it settles as dewdrops on grass, leaves, windows and other surfaces.

FACT FILE

- Caution: At 29°C to 34°C – physical activity may cause fatigue
- Extreme Caution: At 35°C to 41°C – long exposure can cause heat cramps and/or exhaustion
- Danger: Above 41°C – can lead to possible heat stroke with long exposure; heat exhaustion and heat cramps are likely

Heat Index

The heat index combines temperature and relative humidity to give an idea of what it would feel like under normal-to-low humidity conditions. High and dangerous heat indices occur mostly during summer.

Dew Point

The temperature at which the air becomes saturated is called the dew point. If the temperature falls below the dew point, the moisture in the air condenses.

Storming the Skies

Storms are one of the most fascinating and dangerous of all weather conditions. Thunderstorms can uproot trees, while cyclones can destroy entire towns. Storms show weather at its wildest!

▲ *A tropical storm occurs in tropical regions. It has gusty winds, strong enough to uproot trees.*

Long and Short of it

Storms vary in size and duration. The smallest ones – tornadoes and thunderstorms – usually affect areas of about 25 square kilometres and last for a few hours. The largest storms – hurricanes or cyclones – may affect whole continents and last for weeks.

Devastating Power

Storms show us nature's awesome power. The total energy from one thunderstorm can be even greater than that released by an atomic bomb! While we cannot control storms, we can predict them to prevent widespread destruction.

Turning Tornadoes

The tornado in the Wizard of Oz carried Dorothy to a new land. While tornadoes in real life can't do that, they can still be quite devastating. In a tornado, the wind column forms a narrow funnel that spins rapidly and is in contact with the ground.

▶ *Most tornadoes in the Northern Hemisphere spin counter-clockwise, while in the Southern Hemisphere they are clockwise.*

▲ *The best way to protect oneself during a tornado is to take cover in the basement, or even under the stairway, unless you have a purpose-built shelter.*

INTERESTING FACT

Hurricanes are called typhoons in the Western Pacific; baguios in the Philippines; willy-willies in Australia; and cyclones in India. The word 'hurricane' itself comes from a West Indian name.

FACT FILE

- Tornado speeds can reach up to 300 mph (483 kph)
- Hurricane speeds are over 74 mph (119 kph)
- Tropical storms occur at 39 mph (63 kph)
- Gales are between 28 and 55 knots (32-63 mph)

Hurried Hurricane

Hurricanes are violent, spiralling storms that are set off when warm moist air rises over the sea to form huge clouds. More air rushes in below the rising air and starts to spiral up at high speeds, accelerating the cycle. When these fierce winds hit land, they destroy everything in their path.

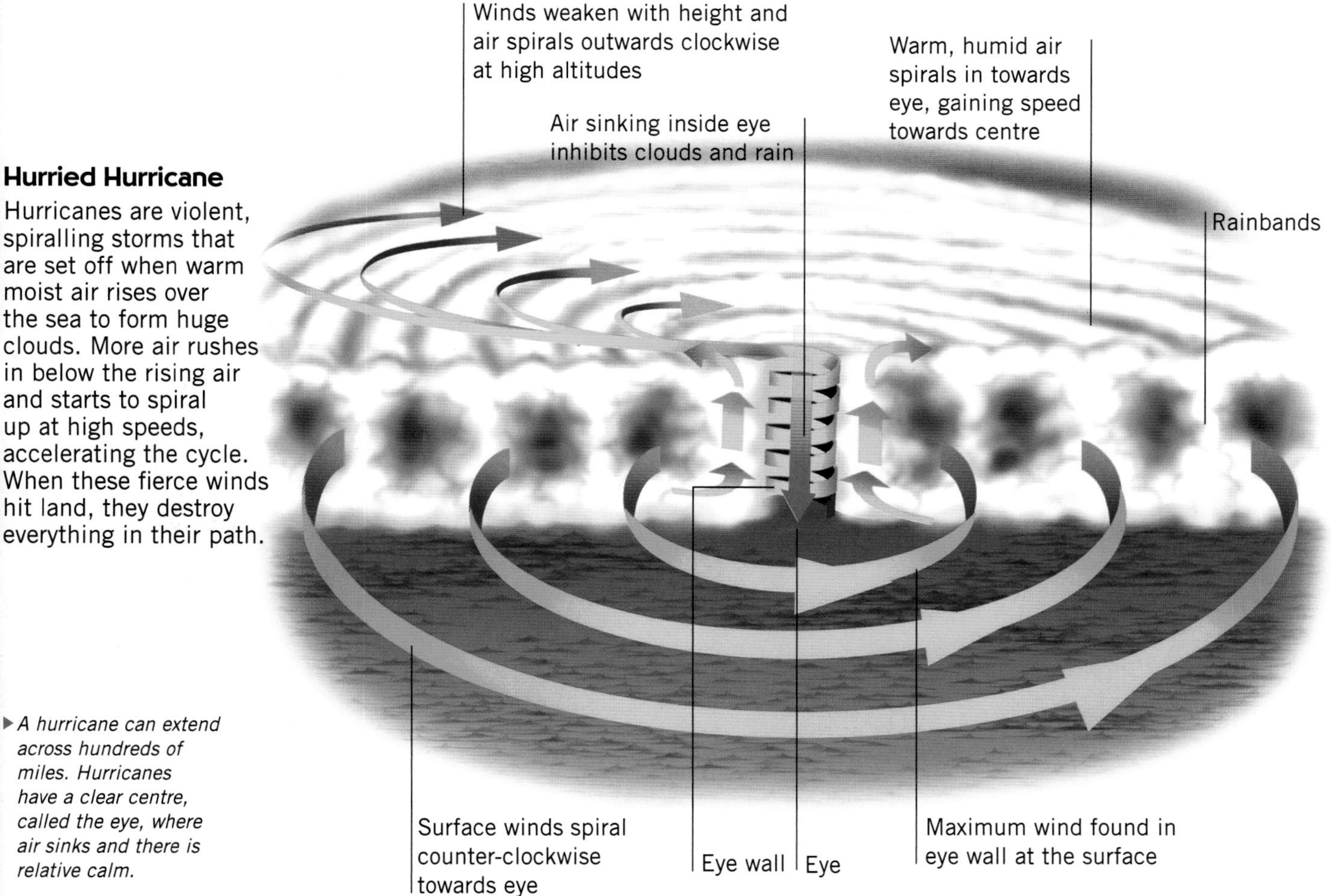

▶ *A hurricane can extend across hundreds of miles. Hurricanes have a clear centre, called the eye, where air sinks and there is relative calm.*

Thunder and Lightning

Thunderstorms are violent, short-lived weather disturbances. They occur when layers of warm, moist air rise in large, swift updrafts to cooler regions of the atmosphere.

Downdraft of Wind

As it rises, the moisture condenses to form towering clouds. When the droplets become very heavy, a downpour follows. Columns of cooled air then sink earthward, striking the ground with strong winds or a thunderstorm.

Lightning Flash

Thunderstorms are accompanied by lightning. It is caused when ice crystals in the clouds rub together, creating electricity and causing a flash of lightning. This discharge also heats up air, causing a loud rumble called thunder.

Lightning can strike tall trees setting them alight.

Not all lightning hits the ground. Cloud-to-ground lightning makes up only 10 percent of all lightning. Other types include cloud-to-cloud and those that occur within the same cloud.

Rare Sights

Some rarely seen types of lightning include red sprites and blue jets. However, you cannot see either of these with the naked eye.

◀ *Long metallic rods are often placed on the roofs of tall buildings to prevent lightning from damaging them. The rods intercept the flashes and guide the current to the ground through cables.*

Striking Force

Lightning strikes tall things, like trees and buildings. So if you are caught in a thunderstorm, crouch on the ground to avoid being hit. Never take shelter under a tree.

INTERESTING FACT

You see lightning long before hearing thunder because light travels faster than sound. To check how far away a storm is, count the seconds between lightning and the sound of thunder. Divide the number of seconds by five to know the distance in miles, or by three for kilometres.

FACT FILE

- As many as 1,800 thunderstorms occur in the world at any given point in time
- Lightning can strike targets 16 or even 40 km away from its parent cloud
- Thunderstorms can produce 100 strikes of lightning every second
- Longest lightning bolt: 190 km, measured in Dallas, US
- Thunderstorm speeds: 19 kph to 161 kph

Weather Wash

Rain is essential for life because it provides water for humans, animals and plants. It is formed from the water vapour present in air. But too much rain can be harmful as well, causing floods that destroy property and life.

Drops Keep Falling

Raindrops vary greatly in size between 0.50-6.40 millimetres in diameter.

▲ The shape of a raindrop depends on its size. Raindrops with a diameter of less than 1 millimetre are round. Larger raindrops become flatter as they fall.

Monsoon Showers

Seasonal rainfall, especially in regions near the tropics, is caused by special winds called monsoons. The monsoon that blows across southern Asia in the summer brings extremely heavy rainfall.

◄ Raincoats and umbrellas help you stay dry even with heavy rainfall.

Flooded Away

A flash flood is caused by sudden, excessive rainfall that causes a river, stream or any other water body to burst its banks. Often, this occurs in a short period of time. These can be deadly, particularly when floods arrive without any warning.

Keeping a Tab

Weather forecasters play a very important role in the reduction of flood losses. By issuing storm and flood warnings, they aim to minimise destruction and the loss of life.

INTERESTING FACT

Weather conditions, combined with a spring tide, produced one of the worst floods on the east coast of England in 1953. Over 300 people lost their lives in this disaster. The flooding was caused by a storm surge.

FACT FILE

- Highest rainfall in a minute: 3.1 cm, at Unionville, US
- Highest rainfall in a day: 182.5 cm, in Foc-Foc, la Reunion, in the Indian Ocean
- Highest rainfall in a month: 930 cm, in Cherrapunji, India
- Highest rainfall in a year: 2,647 cm, in Cherrapunji, India
- Lowest rainfall in a year: 0.03 inches, in Arica, Chile

Boats, rafts and helicopters are used to rescue people marooned by the rising waters in a flood.

As Cold as Can Be

Teeth chattering and bone-chilling temperatures are yet another extreme in the changing moods of the weather. During the Ice Age, the entire Earth was covered with snow. While that period ended about 15,000 years ago, some parts of the Earth like Greenland, Siberia and Antarctica still have snow throughout the year.

▼ *The height of a mountain, the steepness of its slope, and the type of snow on it determine the likelihood of an avalanche.*

Ice Covering

The snow on the ground is constantly changed by wind, temperature and the weight of snow itself. If the snow grows denser, after surviving spring and summer melting, it eventually turns into ice and can form glaciers.

Sliding Avalanches

Even solid ice and layers of snow can be dangerous, as shown by avalanches. An avalanche is a moving mass of snow that may contain ice, soil, rocks and uprooted trees.

Smashing Snow

An avalanche is set off when an unstable mass of snow breaks away from a mountainside and moves downhill. The growing river of snow picks up speed as it rushes down the mountain.

SNOW-COVERED REGIONS (SHADED IN WHITE) ACROSS THE GLOBE...

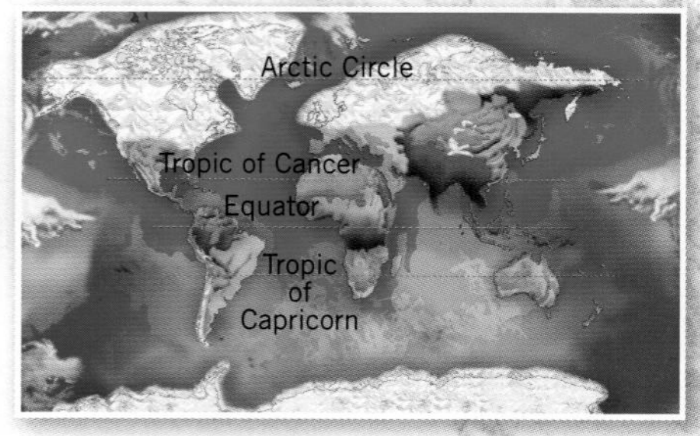

▲ *during the Ice Age.*

▼ *present day.*

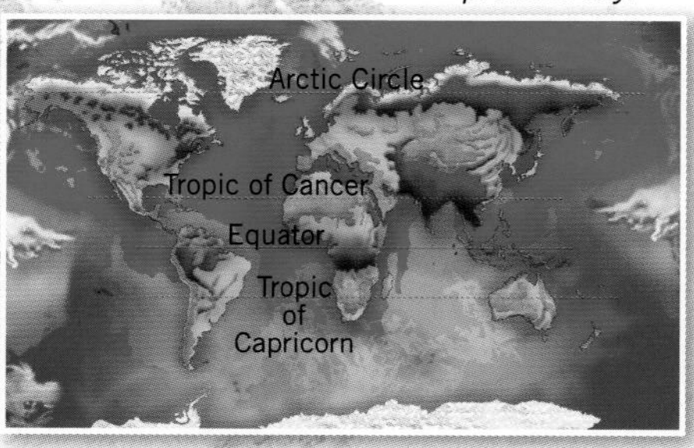

Protective Role

Snow protects crops such as winter wheat from hard frosts and cold, dry winds. People in Greenland and northern Canada live in igloos, or houses built from snow, that give them shelter.

INTERESTING FACT

The climate between the years 1550 and 1750 in England was known as the Little Ice Age, when the winters were so cold that the Thames froze. This allowed for Frost Fairs on the frozen river, complete with tents, sideshows and food stalls. The last such fair was held in the winter of 1813-14.

FACT FILE

- About 90 percent of the world's ice is found in Antarctica
- Snow covers about 23 percent of the Earth's surface
- Frost occurs at temperatures below freezing point
- Avalanche speeds: Up to 245 mph (394 kph)

Snow, Hail and Ice

While rain is the most common form of precipitation, different weather conditions cause the water to fall in different states – be it snow, hail, or even ice. While snow and ice fall only when temperatures touch freezing points, hail can fall during summer too.

White as Snow

If the temperature of clouds is below freezing, ice crystals are formed. These crystals can turn to snow if the temperature of air near the ground is about 2.8°C. If the temperature is in the region of 2.8°C - 3.9°C, the crystals change to sleet or ice pellets.

Ice Storms

Winter storms include ice storms and blizzards. Most ice storms occur when the temperature is just below freezing. In such a storm, precipitation falls as rain, but freezes as it hits the ground. This creates a coating of ice on the ground and streets, making them slippery and often causing traffic accidents.

◀ *Driving snow in blizzards makes it impossible to see more than a short distance. Blizzards can have wind speeds of over 72 kph (45 mph), with near-zero visibility.*

Intricate Snowflakes

Snowflakes are collections of as many as a hundred ice crystals. The heaviest snowfalls occur when the temperature is around the freezing point.

Hailstorms

Yet another form of precipitation is hail. Hail forms when strong air currents carry ice crystals up and down between the top and bottom layers of a thundercloud. The crystals become larger and larger, until they fall to the Earth as hailstones.

▶ *Hailstones form when ice crystals develop from water droplets and continue to grow.*

INTERESTING FACT

Blizzards are snowstorms with high winds and low temperatures. The wind may also pile the snow into huge drifts, thereby blocking roads.

When Storms Strike

Over the years, hurricanes and tornadoes have wreaked havoc upon millions of lives. Here's a look at some of the most devastating storms to have hit mankind.

Big Storm

The biggest storm to hit England occurred in November 1703. The winds are believed to have exceeded 193 kph (120 mph), leaving behind a trail of devastation. As many as 8,000-15,000 people are believed to have been killed in the storm.

▲ *During Hurricane Galveston, the weather bureau office gauge also blew away after recording wind speeds of 160 kph (100 mph). It was a night that completely destroyed Texas City.*

America's Worst

The worst weather disaster in America was the Category 4 hurricane that hit Galveston, Texas, on September 8, 1900. More than 8,000 people died when a 15 foot storm surge flooded the island.

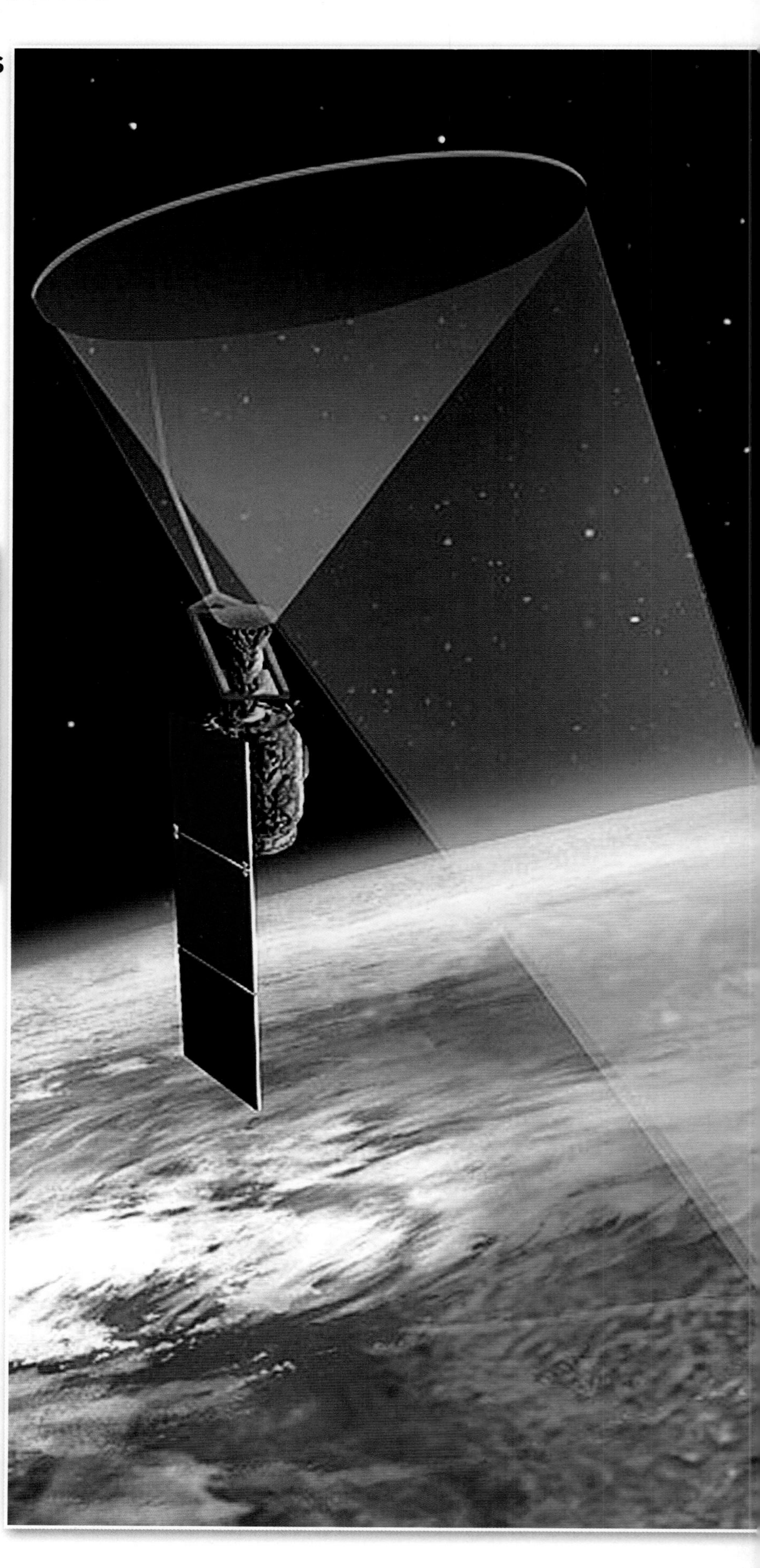

▶ *Since hurricanes cause a lot of damage, scientists try to predict them with the help of many devices. A Scatterometer is one such instrument that is placed on a satellite. It sends out radar beams to Earth and monitors the ones that are reflected back. This in turn is used to measure wind speed and direction.*

Hurricane Hugo

Hurricane Hugo slammed into South Carolina, US, in 1989. The storm began off the coast of Africa and travelled across the Caribbean. Wind speeds as high as 257 kph (160 mph) were recorded. The damages cost the state about $5 billion.

Super Outbreak

The 1974 Super Outbreak spawned 148 tornadoes, the largest number ever produced by a single storm system in the United States. Thirty of these tornadoes were classified as F4 or F5 on the Fujita-Pearson Scale. Before the rampage was over, more than 300 lives were lost over 13 US states and Canada.

INTERESTING FACT

Meteorologists usually give hurricanes special names. These names are reused unless the storm is particularly destructive. They used to be mainly women's names, but since 1979, hurricanes have also been given men's names.

FACT FILE

Hurricane categories

- Category One: Winds 119-153 kph (80-95 mph)
- Category Two: Winds 154-177 kph (96-110 mph)
- Category Three: Winds 178-209 kph (111-130 mph)
- Category Four: Winds 210-249 kph (131-155 mph)
- Category Five: Winds greater than 249 kph (155 mph)

Drought Disasters

A drought is a period of abnormally dry weather, with high temperatures and no rainfall. Droughts affect the agriculture, economy and social structure of a region.

Mercury Rising

Drought areas tend to be hot since lack of rain-producing clouds allows for more sunshine than normal. Higher temperatures and lower humidity levels reduce the likelihood of rainfall. Sparse vegetation further adds to the dry conditions.

Cacti are best suited for dry, drought-like conditions. Their fleshy stem stores water, while the needle-like leaves prevents water loss through evaporation

Severe Loss

Throughout the world, droughts affect more people than any other type of disaster. In some parts of Africa during the 1980s, 25 times the average number of children below the age of five died during a drought.

In areas that are not irrigated, the lack of rain causes farm crops to wither. Livestock may die. Extreme drought can lead to many human deaths.

High Pressure Factor

Areas of sinking air create a condition of high pressure that, in turn, leads to dry spells. If the condition continues for a long period, it is termed as a 'blocking high' and can cause droughts. One such case was the drought of 1976 in England, when the total rainfall in London was just 235 millimetres. Temperatures then soared above 32°C.

Tackling Drought

Creation of artificial lakes have been suggested to beat droughts. Water evaporating from such lakes might initiate a rainfall cycle. Another method that has been tried is cloud seeding, an artificial method of inducing precipitation/rainfall.

Besides aircraft, cloud seeding has been done by rockets, cannons and ground generators.

INTERESTING FACT

In cloud seeding, iodine crystals are scattered among the clouds from an aircraft. The water vapour molecules in the clouds cluster around the crystals and become heavy, causing the overloaded crystals to fall to the Earth as rain. But it works well only in areas where rainfall occurs naturally.

FACT FILE

SEVERE DROUGHTS

- Nile drought in Egypt, 1200-02, over 110,000 people died
- Potato famine in Ireland, 1845-49, killed about 1.5 million people
- Northern China, 1959-61, about 30 million people died
- Biafra, Africa, famine in 1967- 69, killed over one million people

Weather Watch

People try to predict weather to prepare in advance for all the extremes. Over 4,000 years ago, people made forecasts based on the position of the stars. Since then, several instruments and technologies have been developed for more accurate predictions.

Observation Stations

More than 3,500 observation stations record weather conditions on land, using various instruments. Thermometers measure temperature; barometers measure pressure; and anemometers measure wind speed. Weather vanes indicate the direction of winds, while hygrometers measure humidity and rain gauges calculate the amount of rainfall.

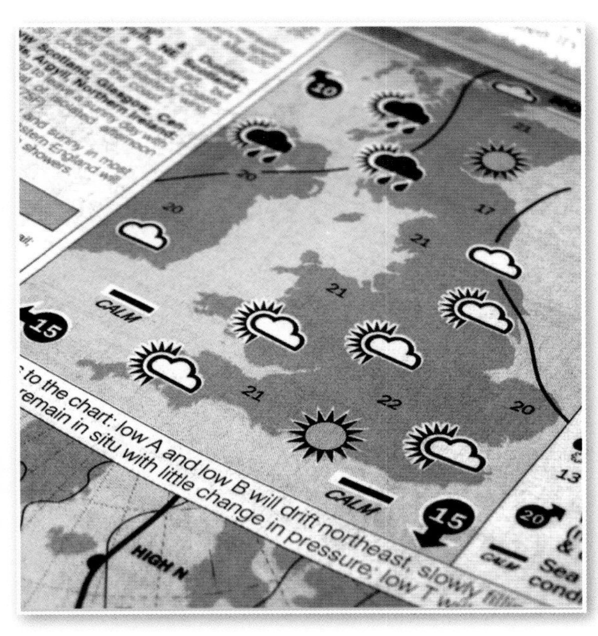

▲ *Weather forecasters on television channels use symbols to tell you what the day will be like in a specific area.*

Picking up Signs

Some observation stations use radar to pick up signs of approaching rain and storms. Satellites also encircle the Earth to convey cloud and temperature patterns. All the data collected is used to create weather maps.

▶ *Every day, observation stations launch two balloons. The balloons are filled with helium, or hydrogen, and measure temperature, air pressure and humidity.*

▲ *Painted wooden boxes provide shelter for weather instruments that need to record the temperature and humidity outdoors, but that also need to be kept away from the rain and direct sunlight.*

INTERESTING FACT

The World Meteorological Organization (WMO), an agency of the United Nations (UN), sponsors the World Weather Watch programme. Through it, weather information is collected by more than 140 nations.

FACT FILE

INSTRUMENTS FOR PREDICTION

- Rain gauge was invented before 300 BC
- Weather vane was developed by 50 BC
- Galileo developed the thermometer in AD 1593
- Edmond Halley made the first weather map in 1686
- The first successful computer forecast was announced in 1950

Time Factor

In the early 1800s, weather forecasting could not be used to warn people of impending storms. Reports were sent by mail, but the storms usually arrived before the post!

Telegraphed Reports

The outdated information system received a boost with the telegraph, which enabled meteorologists to send weather observations quickly. In 1856, France became the first country to start a weather service that relied on telegraphed reports. Great Britain began a similar service in 1860.

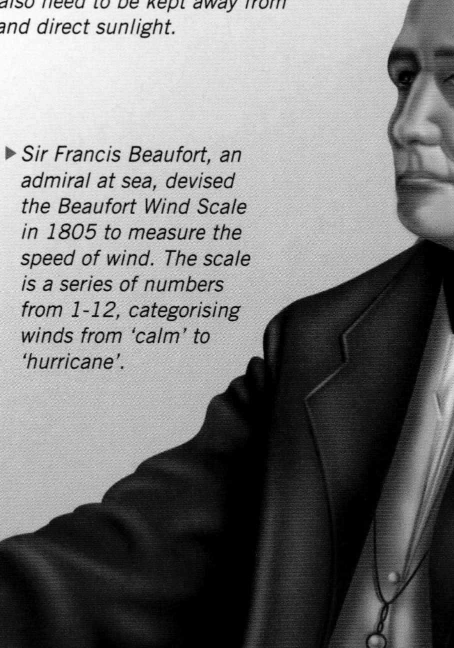

▶ *Sir Francis Beaufort, an admiral at sea, devised the Beaufort Wind Scale in 1805 to measure the speed of wind. The scale is a series of numbers from 1-12, categorising winds from 'calm' to 'hurricane'.*

Eye in the Sky

Meteorologists use special computers for weather forecasting. These computers function swiftly to receive information from weather stations and satellites. They help to build model weather maps and produce a weather forecast.

In Space

Weather stations rely on data from artificial satellites placed in orbit about the Earth. Satellites carry television cameras that take pictures of the Earth. These pictures display the pattern of clouds above the Earth as well as large areas of snow and ice on the ground. The photographs allow meteorologists to spot hurricanes and other storms.

Polar-Orbiting

There are two main kinds of weather satellites – polar orbiting and geostationary. Polar-orbiting weather satellites circle the Earth at altitudes between 800 and 1,400 kilometres. They monitor up to 10 million square kilometres, or about 2 percent of the Earth's surface.

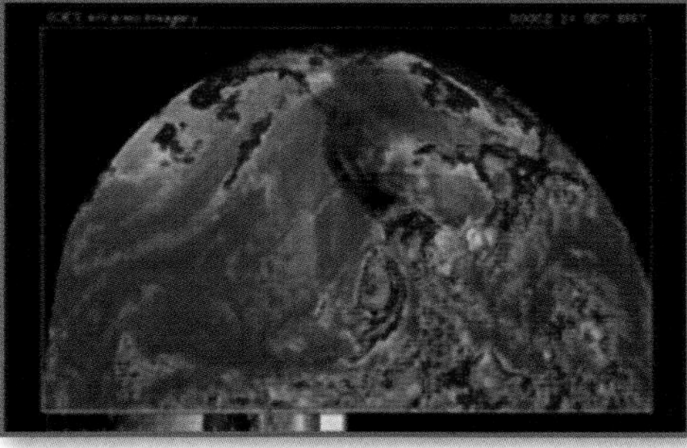

Images from radars are very effective tools for predicting rain. Weather forecasters study the patterns on radar images to provide warnings on severe thunderstorms, tropical cyclones and areas of heavy rainfall

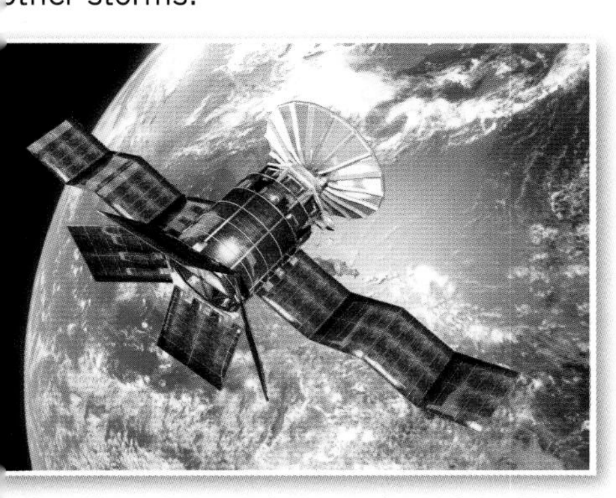

Satellites photograph the surface of the Earth from the skies and these are called satellite images. They show the pattern of winds, clouds and temperature over the Earth. Meteorologists study these images to predict weather.

Weather Planes

Other weather observation facilities include aeroplanes and ships. Special weather planes take measurements of atmospheric conditions.

Weather planes carry a host of instruments on board. They fly over a region and collect data on temperature, pressure and humidity. They can also drop special sensors that collect data from inside a storm.

In Sync

Geostationary satellites, also called geosynchronous satellites, orbit the equator at an altitude of about 35,890 kilometres. At this altitude they can take pictures that cover a much wider area. Pictures from four well-placed geo-stationary satellites can cover the entire Earth at once.

A weather station gets data from satellites, weather planes, observation centres and other sources. Meteorologists keep a track of all this information.

INTERESTING FACT

There are two main types of forecasts – short-range forecasts and extended forecasts. Short-range forecasts predict the weather over the next 18-36 hours, and are updated several times a day. Extended forecasts cover the next 5, 10 or 30 days, but are not entirely accurate.

FACT FILE

- The radar was first used for weather observation in the 1940s
- First weather satellite with a television camera: Tiros I, 1960
- First full-time weather satellite in geostationary orbit: 1974

Changing Weather

Weather conditions across the world have evolved over the years – from the Ice Age to our climate now. The earliest changes were as a result of natural causes, but in the last century, humans have played a crucial role in changing weather patterns.

Ice Age

Nearly 50,000 years ago, the Earth was in the middle of its last Ice Age. Much of the Earth's surface was covered in thick sheets of ice, although the temperatures were not bitterly cold. In fact, the snow cover was constant due to cool summers and mild winters.

Interglacial Period

The Ice Age ended about 15,000 years ago, when the climate warmed up and the ice melted. We now live in an age called the Interglacial Period. But the next Ice Age is round the corner – about 1,000 years away!

Woolly mammoths roamed the Earth during the Ice Age. But as the period ended and the Earth got warmer, it became too hot for the mammoths and they died out about 30,000 years ago.

Slow Change

Changes in climate take place gradually over many years. For example, the climate of several areas in North America was somewhat colder in the 1960s and early 1970s, as compared to the 1930s and 1940s.

Man's Role

The changes in Earth's weather patterns, until recently, were a result of nature. However, in recent times, climate conditions have been negatively affected by various human activities.

Global warming is caused by human activity. High pollution levels from cars and factories cover the surface of the Earth and make it warmer.

INTERESTING FACT

Climate change can be caused by a change in the amount of energy given off by the Sun. Other causes of climatic change include the greenhouse effect and volcanic dust.

FACT FILE

- Rain gauge was invented before 300 BC
- Weather vane was developed by 50 BC
- Galileo developed the thermometer in 1593
- Edmond Halley made the first weather map in 1686
- The first successful computer forecast was announced in 1950

Weather Woes

Changes in weather in recent years, and those predicted over the next 80 years, are largely due to human activity. Environmentalists feel that such changes are likely to pose a threat to our very survival.

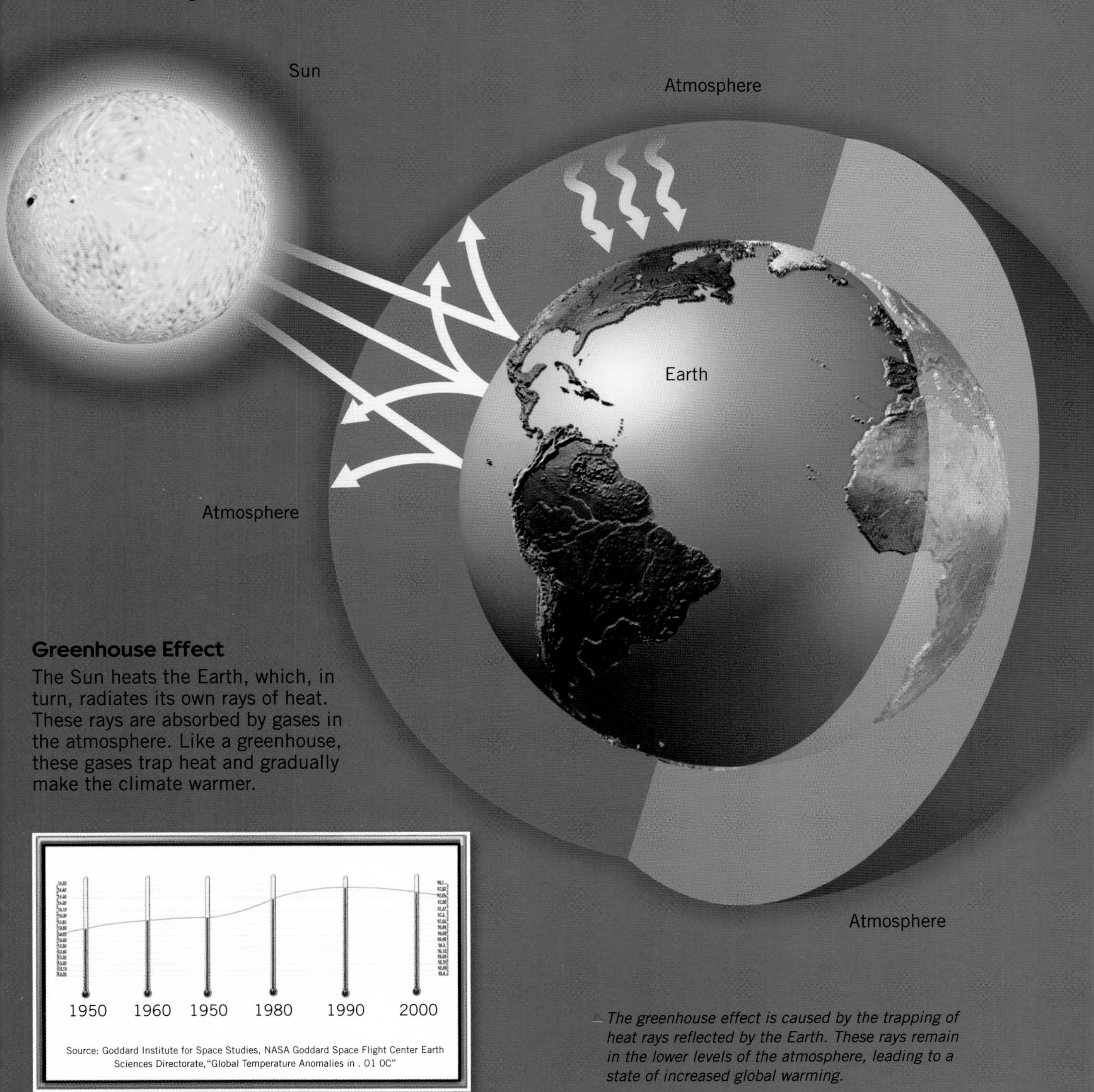

Greenhouse Effect

The Sun heats the Earth, which, in turn, radiates its own rays of heat. These rays are absorbed by gases in the atmosphere. Like a greenhouse, these gases trap heat and gradually make the climate warmer.

The average temperature of the Earth has been rising over the years. This is known as global warming.

The greenhouse effect is caused by the trapping of heat rays reflected by the Earth. These rays remain in the lower levels of the atmosphere, leading to a state of increased global warming.

Catastrophes in Store

Global warming poses a grave danger to all life forms. Rising temperatures are likely to melt glaciers and cause more rain. This in turn, would cause a rise in the sea levels, and subsequently, flooding.

▼ *The world's forests are being stripped of trees at the rate of 24 square km per hour. This is worsening the greenhouse effect, and may lead to major changes in temperature and rainfall patterns.*

▲ *The burning of fossil fuels like coal and petrol produces carbon dioxide and oxides of nitrogen and sulphur*

Acid Rain

Besides rising temperatures, increasing air pollution has also given rise to acid rain. The oxides of sulphur, nitrogen and carbon mix with the moisture in the air to form acids, which are fall to earth as acid rain. This rains is extremely harmful to all forms of life.

INTERESTING FACT

In many places, smoke from factories and vehicle exhausts combine with natural fog to form smog. London, Los Angeles, Tokyo and Mexico City are among the cities that have faced serious smog problems over the years.

FACT FILE

- Global temperatures have risen by over 0.7°C in the last 300 years
- Four out of five of the warmest years ever recorded were in the 1990s
- 1998 was the warmest year globally
- 1999 was the warmest year recorded in the United Kingdom

Weather or What!

The world has often witnessed a range of bizarre weather phenomena, like snowfall in summer, coloured rain, objects falling from the sky, and much more.

Raining Frogs and Peaches

While it may never have literally rained cats and dogs, other bodies have been known to shower down. In August 1814, during a storm near Amiens in France, tiny but live frogs came raining down! A similar case was sighted in 1953, in Massachusetts, US In 1961, Louisiana locals claimed to have witnessed an equally strange downpour of peaches.

Snowy Greens

Various parts of the world have reportedly received snowfall in red, green, yellow and brown colours! These colours were said to be caused by tiny micro-organisms known as Protococcus Nivalis.

El Niño

El Niño refers to the abnormal warming of surface ocean waters in the eastern tropical Pacific. It is believed that El Niño may have led to the 1993 Mississippi floods, the 1998 California floods, and drought conditions in South America, Africa and Australia. Scientists are yet to fully understand the reasons behind the formation of El Niño.

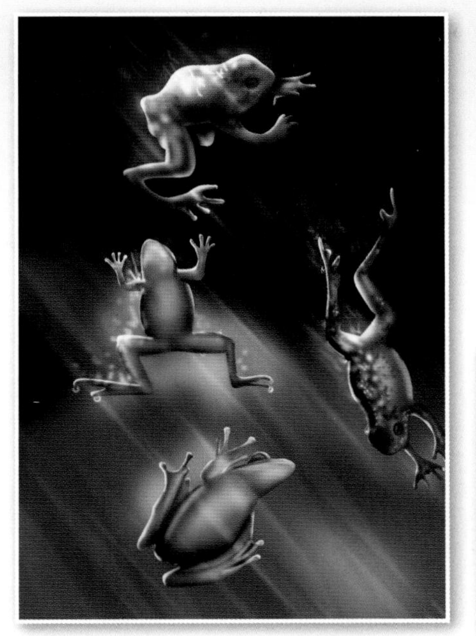

▲ *Apart from frogs, other creatures that have fallen from the skies include flounders, minnows, snails, mussels, maggots, crayfish, geese and even live snakes!*

Colour Washout

There have been quite a few instances of coloured rainfall. During a heavy storm in the Shetland Isles, in March 1935, the rain looked like blue/black ink diluted in water! The explanation offered for this was that of pollution. England too witnessed a red wash on February 21-23, 1903 – caused by dust that blew in from the Sahara.

INTERESTING FACT

It was a case of summer chills in England in 1975, when snow prevented a summer cricket match. Another extreme - in September 1981, the Kalahari Desert in Africa witnessed snowfall for the first time.

Fascinating Facts

Weather forecasting is not foolproof, since 'Mother Nature' never fails to provide surprises. Along with sudden changes in weather conditions, extreme and unusual phenomena make the weather quite unpredictable.

Heat Bursts

Heat bursts are phenomena that at times occur during thunderstorms and make conditions hotter. On September 9, 1994, Glasgow in Scotland recorded a temperature of 19° C at 5:02 am. But a heat burst from a nearby storm shot the thermometer up to 34° C by 5:17 am.

Spouting Water

Another curious occurrence is that of waterspouts. These tornadoes form at sea and are a funnel-like columns of air that suck up sea water and other things in their path. In the past, seamen often mistook waterspouts for monsters rising up from under the ocean!

▼ *People who closely observe a storm brave risky conditions such as high wind, hail, lightning and flying debris.*

Rained Out

The most rain ever recorded in the United Kingdom in one day was on July 18, 1955. It rained as much as 279 millimetres at Martinstown in Dorset. Of course, this is hardly close to the world record of 1,825 millimetres, which fell at Foc-Foc, in la Reunion in the Indian Ocean!

Guiding Light

Weather changes at sea can leave ships stranded. Heavy fog or storm-like situations can make even the most experienced mariners struggle to navigate. To prevent ships running aground or hitting rocks, lighthouses were built.

During a storm, there is a simple way to calculate how many miles away the lightning is. Keep a count of the number of seconds between the strike of lightning and the rumbling of thunder, and divide that number by five to get the answer in miles.

INTERESTING FACT

Storm chasers are people who try to get close to storms for the purpose of observation. Storm-chasing is dangerous work, but most chasers are very passionate about the phenomena and are willing to embrace the risks.

FACT FILE

- Highest barometric pressure: 1083.6 millibars (32 inches); Agata, Siberia
- Odds of being struck by lightning: About 1 in 800,000
- Longest-travelling tornado: 472 km (293 miles), travelled from Missouri to Indiana, US
- Three out of four of all tornadoes hit the United States

Lighthouses are towers that shine a light or sound horns to guide ships to safety while at sea. They are particularly vital during bad weather.